Teacher Edition: Planning and Pacing Guide

Grade 1

Copyright © 2020 by Houghton Mifflin Harcourt Publishing Company

All rights reserved. No part of this work may be reproduced or transmitted in any form or by any means, electronic or mechanical, including photocopying or recording, or by any information storage or retrieval system, without the prior written permission of the copyright owner unless such copying is expressly permitted by federal copyright law. Requests for permission to make copies of any part of the work should be submitted through our Permissions website at https://customercare.hmhco.com/contactus/Permissions.html or mailed to Houghton Mifflin Harcourt Publishing Company, Attn: Intellectual Property Licensing, 9400 Southpark Center Loop, Orlando, Florida 32819-8647.

Common Core State Standards © Copyright 2010. National Governors Association Center for Best Practices and Council of Chief State School Officers. All rights reserved.

This product is not sponsored or endorsed by the Common Core State Standards Initiative of the National Governors Association Center for Best Practices and the Council of Chief State School Officers.

Printed in the U.S.A.

ISBN   978-0-358-11194-8

2 3 4 5 6 7 8 9 10   0877   27 26 25 24 23 22 21 20

4500797960   C D E F G

If you have received these materials as examination copies free of charge, Houghton Mifflin Harcourt Publishing Company retains title to the materials and they may not be resold. Resale of examination copies is strictly prohibited.

Possession of this publication in print format does not entitle users to convert this publication, or any portion of it, into electronic format.

Advocates for Excellence

To develop *Into Math*, we listened to teachers like you, who told us about their unique classroom challenges. Thanks to their voices, *Into Math* is more than just aligned to standards; it was built specifically to help you and your students succeed in the classroom and on high-stakes assessments.

Into Math was developed by a team of esteemed researchers and practitioners. These leaders work tirelessly to evolve instructional practices and advocate for clearer, more holistic, flexible, and active methodology in the classroom.

Edward B. Burger, PhD, is a mathematician who is also the president of Southwestern University in Georgetown, Texas. He is a former Francis Christopher Oakley Third Century Professor of Mathematics at Williams College, and a former vice provost at Baylor University. He has authored or coauthored numerous articles, books, and video series; delivered many addresses and workshops throughout the world; and made many radio and television appearances. He has earned many national honors, including the Robert Foster Cherry Award for Great Teaching. In 2013, he was inducted as one of the first fellows of the American Mathematical Society.

Juli K. Dixon, PhD, is a professor of mathematics education at the University of Central Florida (UCF). She has taught mathematics in urban schools at the elementary, middle, secondary, and post-secondary levels. She is a prolific writer who has published books, textbooks, book chapters, and articles. A sought-after speaker, Dr. Dixon has delivered keynotes and other presentations throughout the United States. Key areas of focus are deepening teachers' content knowledge and communicating and justifying mathematical ideas. She is a past chair of the National Council of Teachers of Mathematics Student Explorations in Mathematics Editorial Panel and a member of the board of directors for the Association of Mathematics Teacher Educators. You can find her on social media at @TheStrokeOfLuck.

Timothy D. Kanold, PhD, is an award-winning international educator, author, and consultant. He is a former superintendent and director of mathematics and science at Adlai E. Stevenson High School District 125 in Lincolnshire, Illinois. He is a past president of the National Council of Supervisors of Mathematics (NCSM) and the Council for the Presidential Awardees of Mathematics (CPAM). He has served on several writing and leadership commissions for National Council of Teachers of Mathematics during the past two decades, including the *Teaching Performance Standards* task force. He presents motivational professional development seminars worldwide with a focus on developing professional learning communities (PLCs) to improve teaching, assessing, and learning of *all* students. He has recently authored nationally recognized articles, books, and textbooks for mathematics education and school leadership, including *What Principals Need to Know About Teaching and Learning Mathematics* and *HEART!: Fully Forming Your Professional Life as a Teacher and Leader.* You can find him on social media at @tkanold.

Matthew R. Larson, PhD, is a past president of the National Council of Teachers of Mathematics (NCTM). Prior to serving as president of NCTM, he was the K–12 mathematics curriculum specialist for Lincoln Public Schools (Nebraska) where he currently serves as associate superintendent for instruction. A prolific speaker and writer, he is the coauthor of more than a dozen professional books. He was a member of the writing teams for the major publications *Principles to Actions: Ensuring Mathematical Success for All* (2014) and *Catalyzing Change in High School Mathematics: Initiating Critical Conversations* (2018). Key areas of focus include access and equity and effective stakeholder communication. He has taught mathematics at the secondary and college levels and held an appointment as an honorary visiting associate professor at Teachers College, Columbia University. You can find him on social media at @mlarson_math.

Steven J. Leinwand is a principal research analyst at the American Institutes for Research (AIR) in Washington, DC, and has nearly 40 years in leadership positions in mathematics education. He is a past president of the National Council of Supervisors of Mathematics and served on the National Council of Teachers of Mathematics Board of Directors. He is the author of numerous articles, books, and textbooks and has made countless presentations with topics including student achievement, reasoning, effective assessment, and successful implementation of standards. You can find him on social media at @steve_leinwand.

Jennifer Lempp is an author and educational consultant. She also currently serves as a coordinator in Fairfax County Public Schools, Virginia. She has taught at the elementary and middle school levels and served as a math coach for many years. She is Nationally Board Certified in Early Adolescence Mathematics and has facilitated professional development at the local, state, and national level on math workshop as a model for differentiated mathematics instruction. You can find her on social media at @Lempp5.

Program Consultants

English Language Development Consultant

Harold Asturias is the director for the Center for Mathematics Excellence and Equity at the Lawrence Hall of Science, University of California. He specializes in connecting mathematics and English language development as well as equity in mathematics education.

Program Consultant

David Dockterman, EdD, operates at the intersection of research and practice. A member of the faculty at the Harvard Graduate School of Education, he provides expertise in curriculum development, adaptive learning, professional development, and growth mindset.

Blended Learning Consultant

Weston Kieschnick, Associate Partner ICLE, a former teacher, principal, instructional development coordinator, and dean of education, Weston Kieschnick has driven change and improved student learning in multiple capacities throughout his educational career. Now, as an experienced instructional coach and associate partner with ICLE, Kieschnick shares his expertise with teachers to transform learning through online and blended models.

STEM Consultants

Michael Despezio has authored many HMH instructional programs for science and mathematics. He has also authored numerous trade books and multimedia programs on various topics and hosted dozens of studio and location broadcasts for various organizations in the US and worldwide. Recently, he has been working with educators to provide strategies for implementing the Next Generation Science Standards.

Bernadine Okoro is a chemical engineer by training and a playwright, novelist, director, and actress by nature. Okoro went from working with patents and biotechnology to teaching in K–12 classrooms. She is a 12-year science educator, Albert Einstein Distinguished Fellow, original author of NGSS and a member of the Diversity and Equity Team. Okoro currently works as a STEM learning advocate and consultant.

Marjorie Frank An educator and linguist by training, a writer and poet by nature, Marjorie Frank has authored and designed a generation of instructional materials in all subject areas. Her other credits include authoring science issues of an award-winning children's magazine, writing game-based digital assessments, developing blended learning materials, and serving as instructional designer and coauthor of school-to-work software. She has also served on the adjunct faculty of Hunter, Manhattan, and Brooklyn Colleges.

Cary I. Sneider, PhD While studying astrophysics at Harvard, Cary Sneider volunteered to teach in an Upward Bound program and discovered his real calling as a science teacher. After teaching middle and high school science, he settled for nearly three decades at Lawrence Hall of Science in Berkeley, California, where he developed skills in curriculum development and teacher education. Over his career, Cary directed more than 20 federal, state, and foundation grant projects and was a writing team leader for the Next Generation Science Standards.

Math Solutions® & Classroom Advisors

Math Solutions® Program Consultants

Deepa Bharath, MEd
Professional Learning Specialist
Math Solutions
Jupiter, Florida

Nicole Bridge, MEd
Professional Learning Specialist
Math Solutions
Attleboro, Massachusetts

Treve Brinkman
Director of Professional Learning
Math Solutions
Denver, Colorado

Lisa K. Bush, MEd
Sr. Director, Professional Development
Math Solutions
Glendale, Arizona

Carol Di Biase
Professional Learning Specialist
Math Solutions
Melbourne, Florida

Stephanie J. Elizondo, MEd
Professional Learning Specialist
Math Solutions
Ocala, Florida

Christine Esch, MEd
Professional Learning Specialist
Math Solutions
Phoenix, Arizona

Le'Vada Gray, MEd
Director of Professional Learning
Math Solutions
Country Club Hills, Illinois

Connie J. Horgan, MEd
Professional Learning Specialist
Math Solutions
Jerome, Idaho

Monica H. Kendall, EdD
Professional Learning Specialist
Math Solutions
Houston, Texas

Lori Ramsey, MEd
Professional Learning Specialist
Math Solutions
Justin, Texas

Lisa Rogers
Professional Learning Specialist
Math Solutions
Cape Coral, Florida

Derek Staves, EdD
Professional Learning Specialist
Math Solutions
Greeley, Colorado

Sheila Yates, MEd
Professional Learning Specialist
Math Solutions
Sioux Falls, South Dakota

Classroom Advisors

Abbey Len Bobbett
Laguna Elementary School
Scottsdale Unified School District
Scottsdale, Arizona

Rebecca Boden
Grant County Board of Education
Grant County Schools
Williamstown, Kentucky

Nicole Bunger
Centennial Elementary
Higley Unified School District
Gilbert, Arizona

Marsha Campbell
Murray Elementary
Hobbs Municipal Schools
Hobbs, New Mexico

Nichole Gard
Palmyra Elementary
Palmyra R-1 School District
Palmyra, Missouri

Dena Morosin
Shasta Elementary School
Klamath County School District
Klamath Falls, Oregon

Joanna O'Brien
Palmyra Elementary
Palmyra R-1 School District
Palmyra, Missouri

Nora Rowe
Peoria Traditional Elementary
Peoria Unified School District
Peoria, Arizona

Terri Trebilcock
Fairmount Elementary
Jefferson County Public Schools
Golden, Colorado

Table of Contents

Welcome to *Into Math* **PG8**

Content Architecture

Focus, Coherence, and Rigor **PG10**

Creating a Learning Arc **PG11**

Lesson Design **PG12**

Promoting Conceptual Understanding **PG14**

Promoting Perseverance **PG15**

Real-World Relevance **PG16**

Mathematical Practices and Processes **PG17**

Language Development **PG20**

Assessments, Data and Reports

Assess and Act to Accelerate Every Student **PG24**

Assessment Is Only as Good
  as How We Use the Data **PG25**

Interim Growth Measure **PG26**

Dynamic Reporting **PG27**

Module Readiness and Progress **PG28**

Data-Driven Grouping **PG29**

Lesson Practice and Homework **PG30**

Teacher Support

Supporting Best Practices **PG32**

Empowering Teachers **PG34**

Ensuring Access and Equity **PG35**

Building a Culture of Professional Growth **PG36**

Blended Learning That Works **PG37**

Fostering Learning Mindsets **PG38**

Understanding Mindset **PG39**

Unpacking Math Standards **PG40**

Progressions and Algebra Readiness **PG41**

Supporting Intervention Needs **PG42**

Professional Learning References **PG43**

Table of Contents

Pacing Guide PG46

End-of-Year Options PG61

Correlations
      Math Standards PG63
      Mathematical Practices and Processes PG66

Problem Types PG69

Differentiated Support Using *Do The Math* PG76

Manipulatives and Tools PG79

Unit Performance Assessments PG83

Into Math Solutions and Components PG90

Academic Notebooks and Math Journals
      My Learning Summary Anchor Charts PG92
      Interactive Glossary PG112

Index PG124

Welcome to

HMH | into **Math**™

Perseverance Powers Student Growth

Designed from the ground up to meet the high expectations of Mathematics Standards, *Into Math* is the only solution built to track, predict, and propel growth for all your students in kindergarten through grade 12.

The Outcomes You Want

The *Into Math* system produces measurable outcomes:

- **students** who have mastered rigorous standards, equipped with skills to persevere when presented with challenging, real-world problems
- **teachers** who grow as professionals, able to apply current research-based strategies and best practices
- **educators** who leverage data to differentiate and adapt, ensuring success in high-stakes assessments
- **families** that use accessible tools to support learning at home

What Makes *Into Math* Students *Unstoppable*?

The *Into Math* system maximizes student growth by helping teachers deliver high-quality instruction while monitoring every student's success.

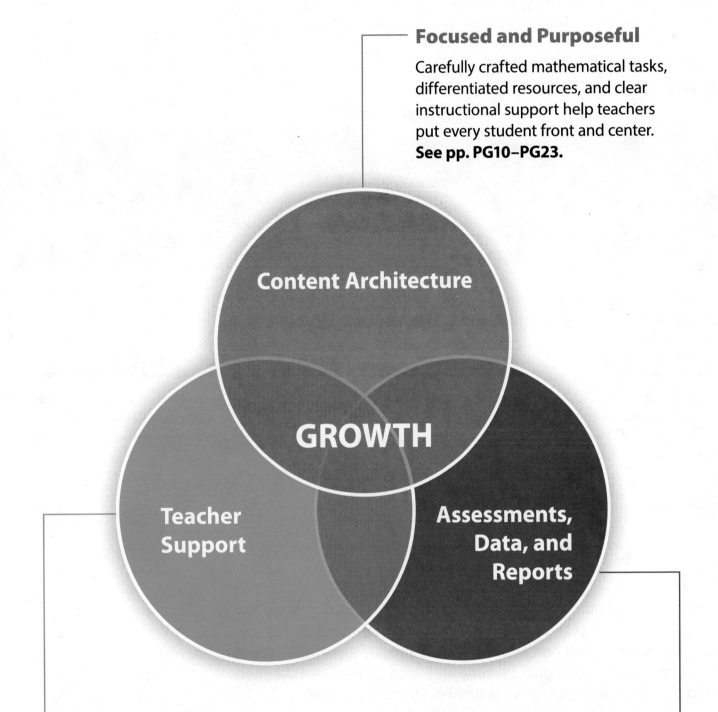

Focused and Purposeful

Carefully crafted mathematical tasks, differentiated resources, and clear instructional support help teachers put every student front and center. **See pp. PG10–PG23.**

Ongoing and Relevant

Embedded support, classroom videos, resource libraries, and coaching provide learning opportunities for teachers of all levels. **See pp. PG32–PG42.**

Integrated and Actionable

Autoscored assignments and assessments help educators make informed instructional decisions. **See pp. PG24–PG31.**

Content Architecture

Focus, Coherence, and Rigor

In *Into Math*, the progression of topics forms coherent learning arcs. The learning arcs are designed to build a foundation of conceptual understanding before teaching procedures. Opportunities for application occur throughout. An emphasis is placed on connections between concepts and skills. The learning arcs ensure delivery of rigorous instruction.

Learning Arc

Application Throughout

CONCEPTUAL	CONCEPTUAL AND PROCEDURAL	PROCEDURAL
Build Understanding	Connect Concepts and Skills	Apply and Practice

To help you visualize the arc and teach with purpose, *Into Math* has three types of lessons, each with a different focus and containing certain learning task types:

Build Understanding

Conceptual These lessons focus on opportunities for students to make sense of the mathematics and build conceptual understanding with real-world context.

- Spark Your Learning
- Build Understanding

Connect Concepts and Skills

Bridging These lessons focus on having students connect different conceptual representations, approaches, or strategies to more efficient procedures.

- Spark Your Learning
- Build Understanding
- Step It Out

Apply and Practice

Procedural These lessons focus on opportunities for students to develop procedural fluency and to apply concepts and procedures.

- Step It Out

Learning Tasks

Spark Your Learning tasks promote conceptual understanding. During these low floor/high ceiling tasks, students leverage prior learning and select manipulatives or representations that serve as their entry point. Teachers provide just-in-time support, helping students engage in meaningful discourse and learn to persevere. Teachers lead the class to shared understanding in a student-centered environment.

Build Understanding tasks are learning opportunities designed to help students understand lesson concepts. Teachers take a more active role, guiding discussion during whole-class instruction.

Step It Out tasks build upon students' conceptual understanding to promote procedural understanding and fluency. Teachers help students understand why the procedures are efficient and how they can be applied to solve similar problem types.

Creating a Learning Arc

Juli K. Dixon, PhD
Professor, Mathematics Education
University of Central Florida
Orlando, Florida

Teaching with Coherence

For students to make the most of their mathematics education, topics should be taught with coherence. This means that topics should be taught as connected ideas rather than within individual silos. Consider strategies for addition. Linking counting strategies with grouping strategies like making a ten in grade 1 supports students to develop fluency with basic facts, setting the stage to make sense of adding and subtracting with regrouping in grade 2.

A benefit of making connections within different mathematical topics is that students have multiple pathways to retrieve what they learned and therefore rely less on rote memorization. For example, students can use counting strategies like *counting on from the larger number,* to recognize that when counting on from a number close to ten, it might be easier to make a group of ten to add (see Figure 1).

Connecting Concepts and Procedures

Rigor describes the important balance between concepts and procedures. While balance is important, so is the order with which concepts and procedures are addressed. Concepts must be taught before procedures; otherwise, there is no motivation to make sense of the mathematics prior to using more efficient processes.

Figure 1 from Grade 1, Lesson 1.4

Consider subtracting multi-digit numbers without a deep understanding of place value. If students are taught the procedure to:

- line up the numbers,
- subtract the ones,
- subtract the tens, and
- subtract the hundreds

prior to understanding place value, then students may make the error of subtracting the digit with the lesser value from the digit with the greater value regardless of which "number" is "on top". This confusion often comes from students not understanding that when ones are subtracted from ones, then tens from tens, and then hundreds from hundreds, the values of multi-digit numbers do not change, the numbers are just grouped by place value. Students are less likely to make these errors with procedures when they have an understanding of place value and representing numbers flexibly. The learning arc is complete when concepts are taught first and then those concepts are linked to more efficient processes before the procedures are practiced and applied.

Content Architecture

Lesson Design

Into Math classrooms are different. Lessons are designed to help you incorporate research-based best practices into your instruction. This design is found in the print student books and in the interactive digital lessons, enabling you to utilize either pathway or a blended approach.

SPARK YOUR LEARNING

5-10 minutes

Teachers guide student discussions, help students persevere as they work together on a mathematical task, and build shared understanding by selecting students to explain their reasoning.

Spark Your Learning

The points scored in baseball games are called runs. The blue team scores 5 runs. The red team scores 1 more run than the blue team. How can you show the number of runs each team scores?

LEARN TOGETHER

5-10 minutes per task

Teachers facilitate learning during whole-group instruction, which ensures that students continue to play an active role in sharing their reasoning and understanding. In *Step It Out* features, students connect important processes and procedures to mathematical concepts.

B. Remember, Elijah has 9 baseball stickers and 8 football stickers. You need to find how many stickers he has. Which doubles fact can help you solve this problem?

○ 7 + 7 = 14

○ 9 + 9 = 18

○ 10 + 10 = 20

CHECK UNDERSTANDING

5 minutes

Teachers utilize this quick formative assessment to determine whether students have mastered lesson content and to identify which differentiation resources will be most useful for each student.

DIRECTIONS: Use this information to answer Parts A, B, and C.

Luc has 13 toy cars. He has 7 red cars. The rest of the cars are green. How many green toy cars does Luc have?

Part A Use the given numbers to complete this addition fact.

Click on the numbers to enter the correct answers in the boxes.

ONLINE

Digital and interactive versions of resources are available on Ed: Your Friend in Learning.

The pacing recommendations within each lesson can be modified based on individual preferences and teaching styles. Yearlong pacing recommendations are in the Pacing Guide starting on page PG46.

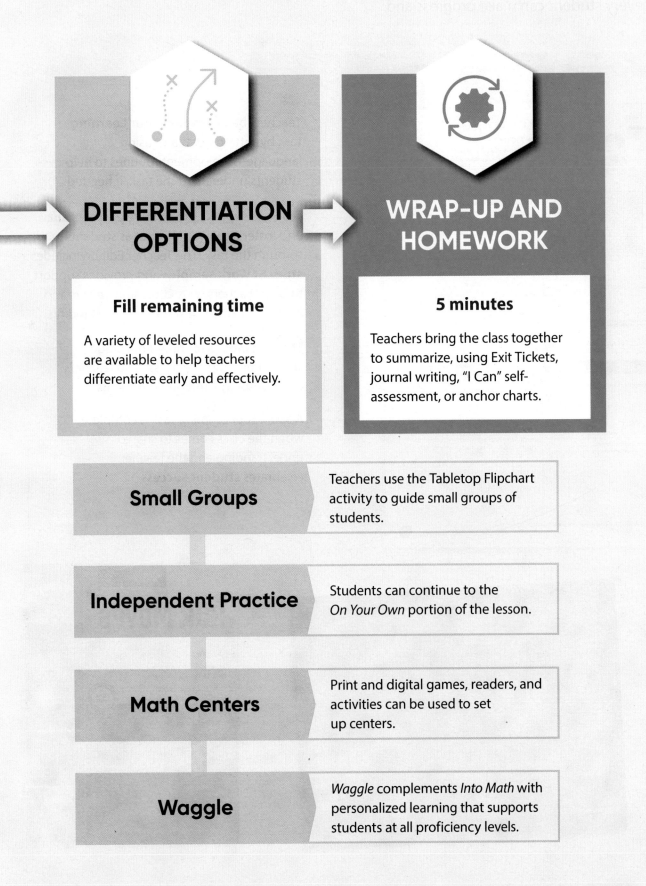

DIFFERENTIATION OPTIONS

Fill remaining time

A variety of leveled resources are available to help teachers differentiate early and effectively.

WRAP-UP AND HOMEWORK

5 minutes

Teachers bring the class together to summarize, using Exit Tickets, journal writing, "I Can" self-assessment, or anchor charts.

Small Groups

Teachers use the Tabletop Flipchart activity to guide small groups of students.

Independent Practice

Students can continue to the *On Your Own* portion of the lesson.

Math Centers

Print and digital games, readers, and activities can be used to set up centers.

Waggle

Waggle complements *Into Math* with personalized learning that supports students at all proficiency levels.

Promoting Conceptual Understanding

Not All Tasks Are Equal. The *Spark Your Learning* tasks have been carefully crafted to promote reasoning and problem solving. The tasks can be solved using various solution strategies and have a low floor and a high ceiling to ensure every student can make progress and build understanding.

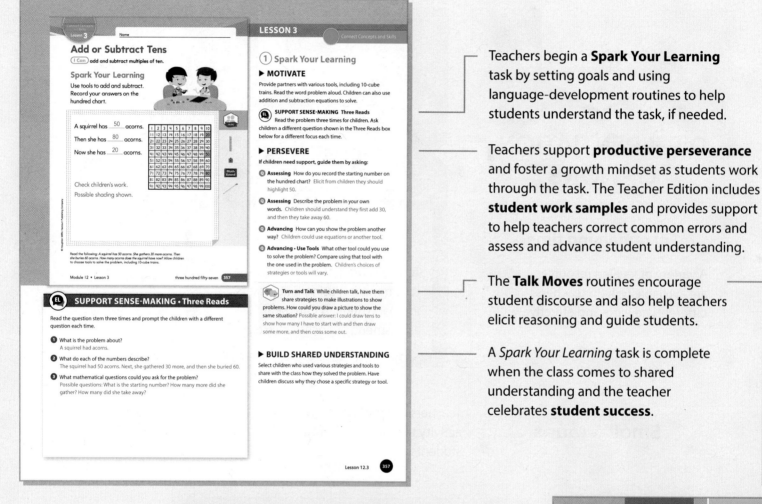

Teachers begin a **Spark Your Learning** task by setting goals and using language-development routines to help students understand the task, if needed.

Teachers support **productive perseverance** and foster a growth mindset as students work through the task. The Teacher Edition includes **student work samples** and provides support to help teachers correct common errors and assess and advance student understanding.

The **Talk Moves** routines encourage student discourse and also help teachers elicit reasoning and guide students.

A *Spark Your Learning* task is complete when the class comes to shared understanding and the teacher celebrates **student success**.

See It in Action
Professional Learning support includes classroom videos with hints, tips, and commentary from experts and authors.

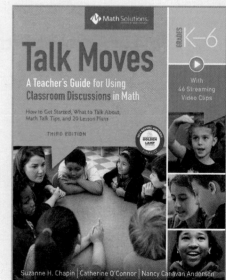

Juli K. Dixon, PhD
Professor, Mathematics Education
University of Central Florida
Orlando, Florida

Promoting Perseverance

Rigorous Tasks

There is little argument that students need to learn to persevere. Where the struggle exists is in determining the pathway to this important outcome. It begins with a good task. Good tasks are rigorous. Providing rigorous tasks sets the stage for students to engage in worthwhile activity around learning mathematics. Good tasks have "low floors" and "high ceilings" so that students have access to the content regardless of their prior achievement.

A rigorous task is one that supports students to do the sense-making. A goal might be to make connections between concepts and procedures, or possibly to determine a solution process when a procedure for the solution has not yet been introduced. Students are expected to explain and justify their thinking. Rigorous tasks afford students the opportunities to develop productive habits of mind around mathematical problem solving.

Just-in-Time Scaffolding

All too often, with best intentions, teachers or resources undermine the value of a good task by providing scaffolding too early. It is tempting to provide scaffolding to students at the first sign of struggle or even in anticipation of student struggle. However, if the struggle is productive, this scaffolding should be withheld. Instead of providing scaffolding just in case students might need it, scaffolding should be offered just in time, when there is evidence that a student's struggle is no longer productive.

While the opportunity to develop perseverance is reliant on access to good tasks, it is supported during instruction by effective teaching. For students to develop perseverance, they must engage in productive struggle. This means that scaffolding, on the student page or from the teacher, needs to be managed in a way that supports students to do the sense-making.

Scaffolding should be provided when students' engagement with the task is no longer productive or when the students' work is not leading to the learning objective. A key to effective teaching is to know when to provide the scaffolding and when to step aside to allow students to persevere.

Content Architecture

Real-World Relevance

Is your weight on the Moon proportional to your weight on Earth? Am I on track to meet my goal for number of steps walked today? How did people 10,000 years ago incorporate geometric designs into their jewelry? Projects and tasks in *Into Math* are carefully crafted, not only to ensure they have the appropriate level of rigor, but also to ensure students remain engaged and see the relevance of math in the world around them.

Each unit opens with a career-related project that students can work on throughout the unit.

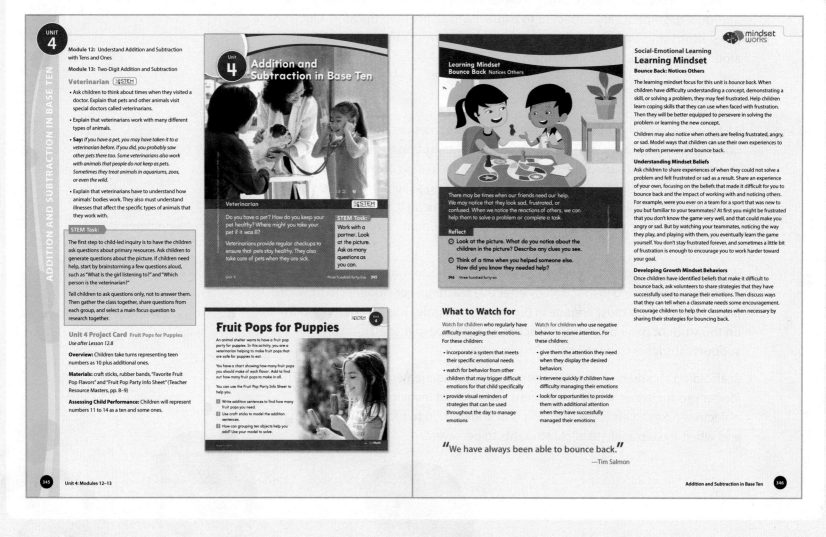

Cross-curricular tasks are found throughout the program, including STEM problems in each module and STEM-themed unit projects.

Opportunities, strategies, and support to help students focus on mindset are embedded in every lesson and in the unit-level projects.

Mathematical Practices and Processes

Into Math provides a focus on Mathematical Practices and Processes aligned to the lesson's learning goal and the tasks that meet the learning goal.

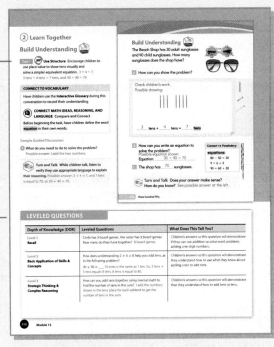

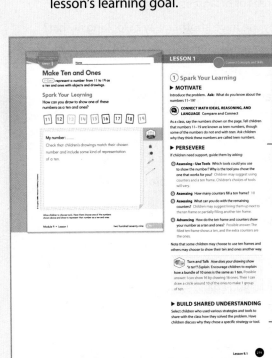

Each lesson focuses on Mathematical Practices and Processes based on the lesson's learning goal.

Each task references a focused Mathematical Practice and Process and includes probing questions to support student engagement and depth of understanding.

Students choose strategies and tools. The Teacher Edition provides additional support with Use Tools questions.

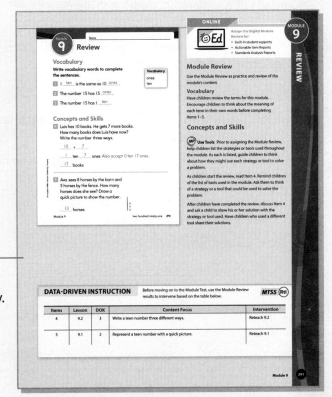

Students solidify their understanding and choose tools strategically. The Teacher Edition provides additional recommendations for student discourse.

Content Architecture

Mathematical Practices and Processes	Questions to Ask:
Make sense of problems and persevere in solving them. • *Spark Your Learning* tasks provide low floor/high ceiling, real-world problems accessible to all students. Students make sense of these problems to plan their solution pathways. • *Build Understanding* tasks present problems with some scaffolding, which supports students while they are making sense of problems. • *Turn and Talk* questions foster collaboration by asking students to discuss their solution pathways or to discuss how they know their solution makes sense.	• What is the problem asking? • How will you use that information? • What other information do you need? • What is another way to solve that problem? • What can you do if you don't know how to solve a problem? • Have you solved a problem similar to this one? • How do you know your answer makes sense?
Reason abstractly and quantitatively. • *Spark Your Learning* tasks provide real-world problems, accessible to all students. Each task is often supported with the language routine *Three Reads* to help students to reason abstractly and to look at quantities and units. • *Build Understanding* and *Step It Out* tasks present problems that require quantitative reasoning. • *Turn and Talk* questions ask students to discuss the representation of the problem and the meaning of the quantities and units with the context of the problem and solution. • *On Your Own* and *More Practice/Homework* include practice problems labeled *Reason*.	• What quantities are referenced? • How are the quantities related? • How can you represent this situation? • How are the quantities and the units related? • What are the correct units for the quantities in the problem? • How do you know your answer is reasonable?
Construct viable arguments and critique the reasoning of others. • *Connect to Vocabulary* provides context and definitions for academic vocabulary. • The language routine *Critique, Correct, and Clarify* has students correct work having a flawed explanation, argument, or solution method. • *Build Understanding* tasks encourage students to describe or explain their reasoning. • *Turn and Talk* questions ask students to discuss a flawed explanation, argument, or solution method. • *On Your Own* and *More Practice/Homework* include practice problems labeled *Construct Arguments* and *Critique Reasoning*.	• Will that method always work? How do you know? • What do you think about what the other student said? • Who agrees or disagrees, and why? • Does anyone have another way of looking at that? • What do you think will happen if…? • When would that not be true? • Does that make sense to you? Why?
Model with mathematics. • *Spark Your Learning* tasks provide students with opportunities to use mathematics they know to represent and solve a problem. • *Build Understanding* and *Step It Out* tasks present problems and then have students decide how to model the problems. • *Turn and Talk* questions ask students to describe or explain their models and why they chose a specific mathematical representation. • *On Your Own* and *More Practice/Homework* include practice problems labeled *Model with Mathematics*.	• Why is that a good model for this problem? • How can you use a simpler problem to help you find the answer? • What conclusions can you make from your model? • Do your results make sense within the context of the problem? • How would you change your model if…?

For a correlation to specific lessons, see pages PG66–PG68.

Mathematical Practices and Processes	Questions to Ask:
Use appropriate tools strategically. • *Unit Openers* include a STEM task that has students use mathematics they know to complete a task and then reflect on strategies and tools they used. • *Spark Your Learning* tasks prompt students to choose tools as part of their solution pathways. Students are asked to explain their choices. • *Build Understanding* and *Step It Out* tasks have students choose tools and describe or explain their choices. • *Module Review* provides an opportunity for students to review the module content and reflect on the full meaning of this practice with a guided discussion. • *Turn and Talk* questions ask students to describe or explain why they chose a specific tool. • *On Your Own* and *More Practice/Homework* include practice problems labeled *Use Tools*.	• What could you use to help you solve the problem? • What strategy could you use to make that calculation easier? • How would estimation help you solve that problem? • Why did you decide to use...?
Attend to precision. • *Build Understanding* and *Step It Out* tasks provide vocabulary once students have explored the concept at point of learning and often are paired with *Connect to Vocabulary*. • The *Interactive Glossary* provides opportunities for students to make sense of vocabulary by having students record in their own words or with examples. • *Step It Out* tasks, *On Your Own*, and *More Practice/Homework* provide opportunities for students to focus on performing calculations accurately and efficiently. • *Turn and Talk* questions provide opportunities for students to communicate precisely to others by using accurate mathematical terms and definitions. • *On Your Own* and *More Practice/Homework* include practice problems labeled *Attend to Precision*.	• How do you know your answer is reasonable? • How can you use mathematics vocabulary in your explanation? • How do you know those answers are equivalent? • What does that mean?
Look for and make use of structure. • *Spark Your Learning* tasks provide opportunities for students to relate to structures they know as a way to make sense of the problem and find a solution pathway. • *Build Understanding* and *Step It Out* tasks connect concepts by showing an example and asking students to explain or describe a structure based on what is shown in the example. • *Turn and Talk* questions ask students to identify, describe, or explain a structure they used to solve a problem. • *On Your Own* and *More Practice/Homework* include practice problems labeled *Use Structure*.	• What rule did you use to make. . . ? • Why can you use that property in this problem? • How is that like...?
Look for and express regularity in repeated reasoning. • *Spark Your Learning* tasks provide opportunities for students to notice repeated calculations and other patterns leading to a general method or shortcut. • *Build Understanding* and *Step It Out* tasks connect repeated reasoning to a new general method or shortcut. • *Turn and Talk* questions ask students to describe or explain their reasoning. • *On Your Own* and *More Practice/Homework* include practice problems labeled *Use Repeated Reasoning*.	• How did you discover that pattern? • What other patterns can you find? • What do you remember about...? • What happens when...? • What if you...instead of...? • What might be a shortcut for...?

Language Development

Language development and the development of mathematical understanding are interdependent. All students must be able to listen, speak, read, write, and converse to meet the rigorous expectations of standards and become proficient problem solvers.

> **B** How can you write an equation to solve the problem?
>
> Equation: _____
>
> **C** The shop has _____ sunglasses.
>
> **Connect to Vocabulary**
>
> **equations:**
>
> $80 - 50 = 30$
>
> $9 = 6 + 3$
>
> $90 = 60 + 30$
>
> 🗣 **Turn and Talk** Does your answer make sense? How do you know?

Before teaching new vocabulary, *Into Math* ensures that students have an opportunity to first build a foundation of conceptual understanding. Vocabulary emerges once students have the conceptual foundation on which to build meaning.

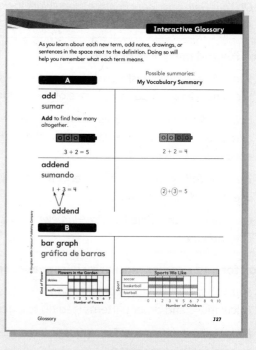

Vocabulary cards can be used with vocabulary games. The eGlossary includes vocabulary terms and definitions translated into ten different languages.

The Interactive Glossary provides space for students to make graphic organizers or drawings for each new vocabulary term.

Harold Asturias
Director, Center for Mathematics
Excellence and Equity
Lawrence Hall of Science
University of California
Berkeley, California

"We must explicitly teach the language of mathematics in order to give students—especially English learners—access to mathematics."

Math is a second language for ALL students. *Into Math* is built on four design principles from the Stanford Center for Assessment, Learning, and Equity (SCALE). These four design principles promote the use and development of language as an integral part of instruction.[1]

1 Support Sense-Making

Scaffold tasks when needed, being sure to amplify (instead of simplify) language for students.

2 Optimize Output

Help students describe their mathematical reasoning and understanding.

3 Cultivate Conversation

Facilitate mathematical conversations among students.

4 Maximize Linguistic and Cognitive Meta-Awareness

Help students evaluate their use of language and see how mathematical ideas, reasoning, and language are connected.

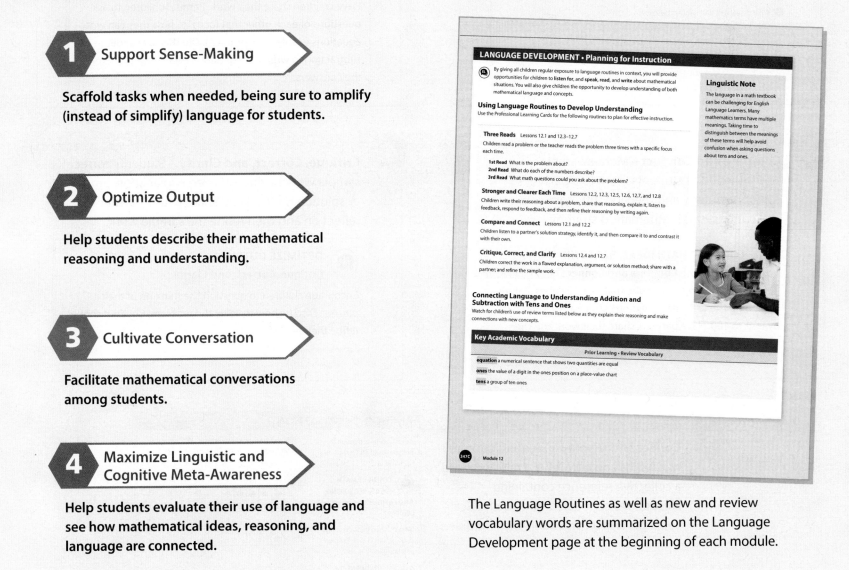

The Language Routines as well as new and review vocabulary words are summarized on the Language Development page at the beginning of each module.

---

1) J. Zwiers, et al., *Principles for the Design of Mathematics Curricula: Promoting Language and Content Development* (Stanford, CA: Stanford University, 2017).

Content Architecture

Language Development

The **5 Routines for Language Development** help teachers promote the design principles during instruction with routines that are structured, but adaptable, in a format for amplifying, assessing, and developing students' language. These Routines provide opportunities for students to listen, speak, and write about mathematical situations with practices that are appropriate and effective for all **language proficiency levels**.

1 **Three Reads** – To ensure understanding of mathematical questions, students read a problem three times with a specific focus each time.

> **(EL) SUPPORT SENSE-MAKING • Three Reads**
>
> Read the problem stem three times and prompt the children with a different question each time.
>
> **1** What is the problem about?
> Meg has some toy rings. She has some and then she gets some more.
>
> **2** What do each of the numbers describe?
> 20 is the number of toy rings she gets and 50 is the number of toy rings she has at the end.
>
> **3** What math questions could you ask about the problem?
> Possible questions: How many more rings does she get? How many does she have in all? How many did she start with?

2 **Stronger and Clearer Each Time** – Students use structure to write their reasoning behind a problem, share and explain their reasoning, listen to and respond to feedback, and then write again to refine their reasoning.

> **(EL) CULTIVATE CONVERSATION**
> **Stronger and Clearer**
>
> Have children share their work. Remind children to ask questions of each other that focus on how they can write equations to solve this problem. Did they use addition or subtraction to write the equation? Then, have them refine their answers.

3 **Compare and Connect** – Meta-awareness is strengthened as students listen to a partner's solution strategy and then identify, compare, and contrast this mathematical strategy.

> **(EL) CONNECT MATH IDEAS, REASONING, AND LANGUAGE** Compare and Connect
>
> Point out to children each cube train has 10 cubes. Before beginning the task, have children count forward and back by tens to 100. Have partners share their work and then compare and contrast.

4 **Critique, Correct, and Clarify** – Students correct sample work having a flawed explanation, argument, or solution method and share with a partner to reflect on and then refine the sample work.

> **(EL) OPTIMIZE OUTPUT**
> **Critique, Correct, and Clarify**
>
> Encourage children to question the thinking of their partner. Discuss how to solve the problem. Children should refine their responses.

5 **Collect and Display** – Students capture oral words and phrases learned and build a collective reference containing illustrations connected to mathematical concepts and terms within each module.

> **ANCHOR-CHART OPTION**
>
> As you progress through the module, build and display an anchor chart.
>
> **(EL) CONNECT MATH IDEAS, REASONING, AND LANGUAGE** Collect and Display
>
> Have children build their own anchor chart in their Practice and Homework Journal.
>
> A completed chart for the module is shown here.

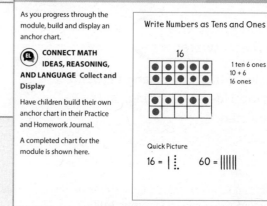

Teacher Tabletop Flipcharts, designed for reteaching and reinforcing each lesson's content with small groups, contain leveled scaffolding and support for English learners. These scaffolding suggestions ensure teachers will maintain the rigor and cognitive complexity level required for mathematical reasoning when supporting English learners.

Three proficiency levels

(EL) Proficiency Level

Beginning
Write the numbers 11 to 19 on individual index cards and spread them out on a table. Have children point to the teen number as you read it to them. Then have children repeat the number back to you. Be sure children say the words correctly (e.g., *fifteen*, not *fifty*, or *fourteen*, not *forty*.)

Intermediate
Have children describe their representation of a teen number using sentence starters. (e.g., I can connect _____ cubes to make one _____. My single cubes are like the _____.)

Advanced
Have children represent any teen number with cubes, then explain how to write the number in three different ways.

School Home Letters are available in English, Spanish, Haitian-Creole, and Portuguese.

Assessments, Data, and Reports

Assess and Act to Accelerate Every Student

To help students grow, we must first understand where they are and what they need. Assessment tools embedded throughout *Into Math* monitor individual student progress and help teachers understand where students are tracking at any given point. The snapshot below represents what a student's data profile could look like after using *Into Math* for 95 days.

Administered three times per year, this adaptive assessment provides a Quantile® score and is predictive of performance on high-stakes assessment.

These short assessments diagnose prerequisite skills readiness, inform grouping, and measure progress.

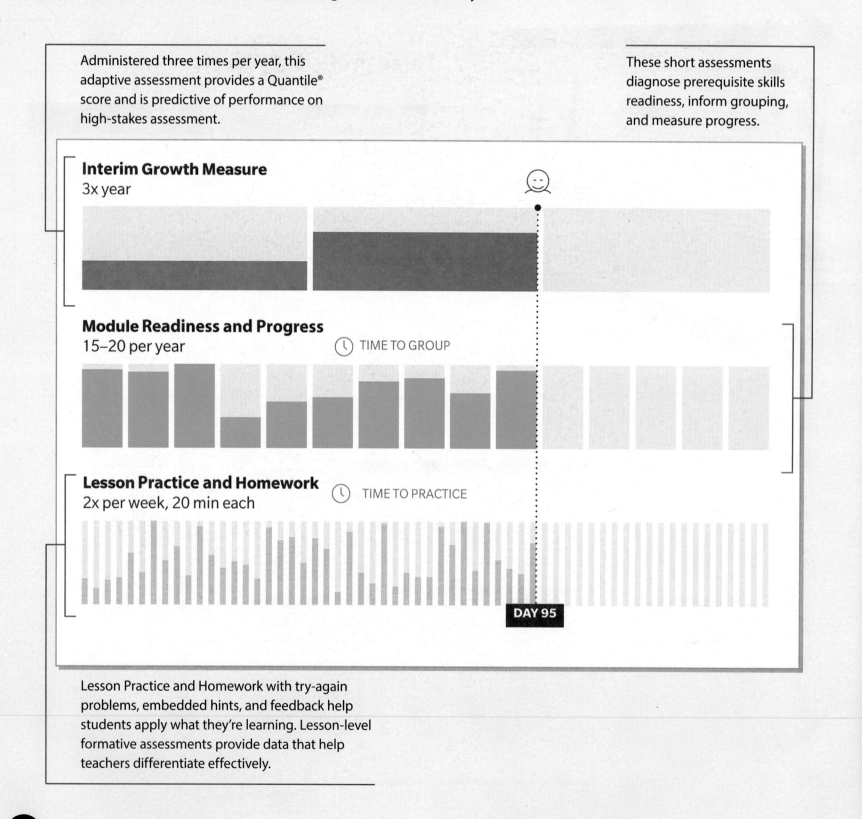

Interim Growth Measure
3x year

Module Readiness and Progress
15–20 per year   ⏱ TIME TO GROUP

Lesson Practice and Homework
2x per week, 20 min each   ⏱ TIME TO PRACTICE

DAY 95

Lesson Practice and Homework with try-again problems, embedded hints, and feedback help students apply what they're learning. Lesson-level formative assessments provide data that help teachers differentiate effectively.

Steven J. Leinwand
Principal Research Analyst
American Institutes for Research
Washington, DC

Assessment Is Only as Good as How We Use the Data

Assessment as Evidence Gathering

We know that effective assessments are far more than just tests we use to help us grade students. Instead, effective assessments are powerful vehicles for gathering evidence of readiness to learn (diagnostic), for learning (formative), and of learning (summative). We also know that the strength and usefulness of the evidence we gather depend on the alignment of these assessments with our standards and our learning goals, as well as on the balance among skills, concepts, and applications and among levels of depth of knowledge found in our assessments.

We plan and we teach. That is, we focus most on our curriculum and our instruction. However, the glue that holds much of our work together and that answers the critical questions about how successful we are being with our planning and teaching is our system of assessments.

Making Effective Use of the Evidence We Collect

Consider the questions to which we all seek reliable answers:

- Are my students ready for the material I'm about to teach?
- Is what I hoped to convey understood by my students? How well? What appears to need more reinforcement?
- Have my instructional strategies worked, or do they need adjustment?
- Can my students apply what they have learned?
- Have my students made connections with previously learned skills and concepts?
- Do I have to reteach the material?
- Which students need additional attention?
- What specific interventions are needed?
- Has previously taught material been retained?

We use diagnostic, formative, and summative assessments to gather data that help us answer each of these questions, but it is how these data are used that makes all the difference. For example, teachers regularly adjust their lesson plans and teach prerequisite skills and concepts on the basis of diagnostic assessments. Similarly, teachers celebrate success, group students, and reteach content based on formative assessments. Far too infrequently, teachers use summative assessments to identify class and individual problems and gaps, reteach in different ways, and incorporate additional instruction into upcoming units. Finally, teachers use all of these data to revise teaching activities and pacing.

Ed: Your Friend in Learning

Teachers are the key to ensuring student growth. That's why we've designed *Into Math* with teachers' needs front of mind. Ed: Your Friend in Learning is your new friend in teaching, designed specifically to help you regain time and easily plan, create, and implement high-impact instruction all from one simple platform.

Within *Into Math*, data collection is automated; differentiation is targeted, clear, and easy to use; and professional development is embedded. The experience is both intuitive and customizable for teachers, allowing for simplicity in all areas of instruction.

Interim Growth Measure

This powerful growth measure assessment is designed to be administered in 40 minutes, three times per year. The system utilizes a secure bank of assessments to adapt to each student's ability and maps progress on the Quantile Framework®.

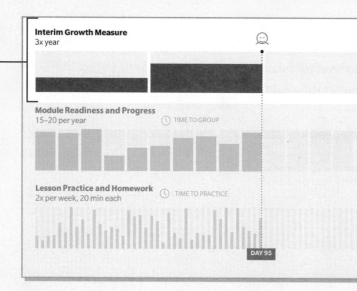

Interim Growth Measure
3x year

Module Readiness and Progress
15–20 per year   TIME TO GROUP

Lesson Practice and Homework
2x per week, 20 min each   TIME TO PRACTICE

DAY 95

Students can skip questions if needed and access read-aloud support. Feedback that encourages perseverance helps to motivate students.

Dynamic Reporting

Teachers can drill down into data for deeper insights into student performance. Multiple reports and views enable teachers to select those that work best for them, including charts, detailed comparisons, and totals.

Assignment reports show detailed results for each assignment, including an item analysis view.

Standards reports show progress toward mastery of each of the Mathematics Standards.

Quantile® Measure	Tested Proficiency	Growth From Previous Test	State Forecasted Proficiency
1006Q	● Proficient	↗ 116Q	Level 3 (Proficient)
890Q	● Proficient	↗ 41Q	Level 3 (Proficient)
849Q	● Basic	N/A	Level 2 (Basic)

Growth Reports help identify intervention needs and are linked to recommendations and groupings.

Module Readiness and Progress

Whether you use the autoscored digital assessments or the paper-and-pencil versions in the Assessment Guide, the module assessments make it easy for teachers to leverage data. A variety of reports available on Ed: Your Friend in Learning give you unparalleled insight into student performance.

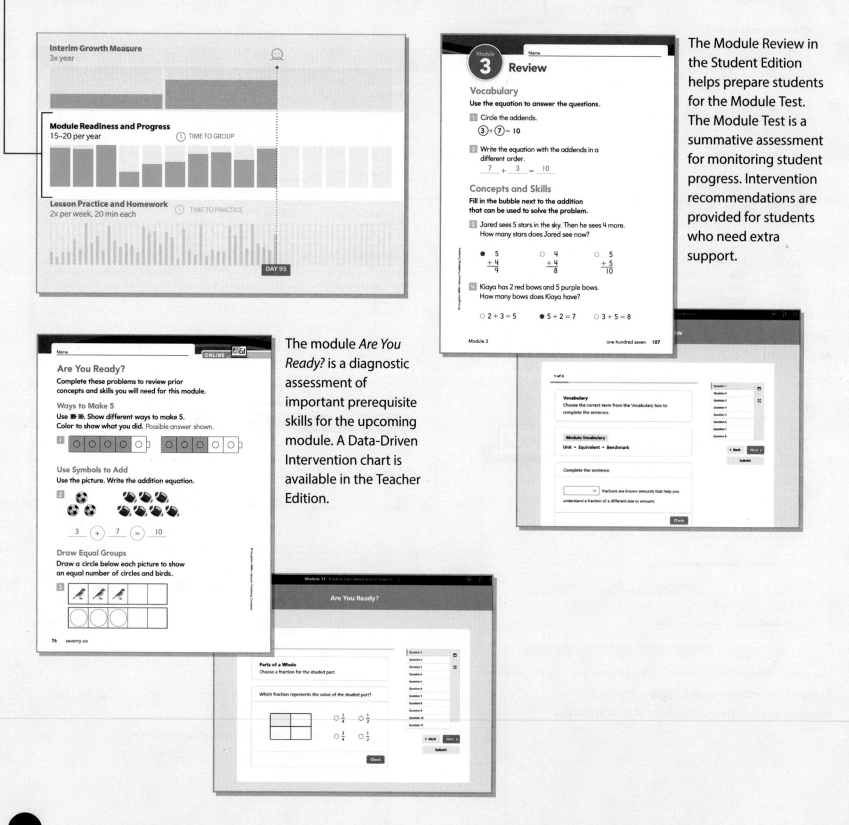

The module *Are You Ready?* is a diagnostic assessment of important prerequisite skills for the upcoming module. A Data-Driven Intervention chart is available in the Teacher Edition.

The Module Review in the Student Edition helps prepare students for the Module Test. The Module Test is a summative assessment for monitoring student progress. Intervention recommendations are provided for students who need extra support.

Data-Driven Grouping

One of the most valuable and time-saving tools for teachers is the online Recommend Groups feature. It synthesizes data from assessments and places students into leveled groups. You can easily modify the recommended groups yourself as needed.

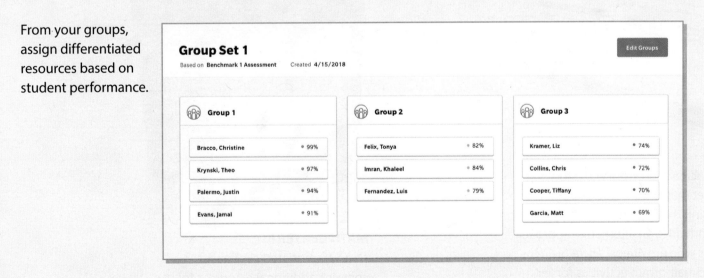

From your groups, assign differentiated resources based on student performance.

Assessments, Data, and Reports

Lesson Practice and Homework

MAKING SURE EVERY STUDENT GROWS Lesson-level formative assessments and the *Into Math* system reports help teachers differentiate, ensuring every student feels appropriately challenged and makes progress toward lesson goals.

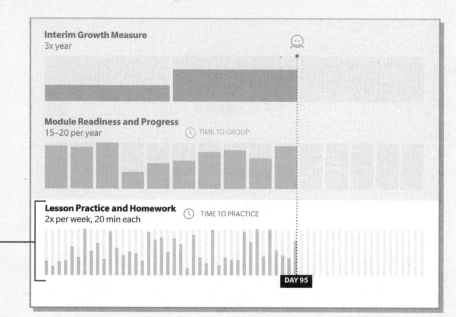

TEACHER EDITION The Teacher Edition shows the variety of differentiated resources available for each lesson.

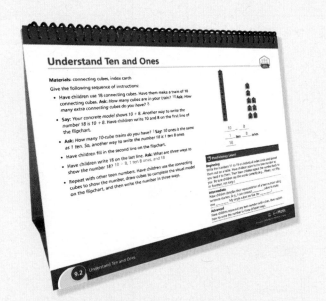

FLIPCHART Teachers can work with students who have not yet mastered lesson content in small groups using the Tabletop Flipchart Mini-Lesson. It provides an alternative approach to help students who are *Almost There* master lesson content. Small-group activities for students who are *On Track* or *Ready for More* are printed in the Teacher Edition.

MATH CENTER KIT

The differentiated centers kit contains additional resources for use in math centers. These resources include games, readers, standards practice, fluency builders, and projects.

Assessments, Data, and Reports

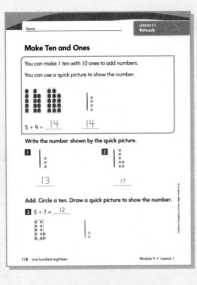

Reteach Worksheet

Interactive RtI Tier 3

LEVERAGE THE POWER OF STUDENT DATA

Interactive versions of Reteach, Challenge, Additional Practice, Fluency, RtI Tier 2, and RtI Tier 3 worksheets can be assigned online, and teachers can see student results in reports.

EMPOWER STUDENTS WITH *WAGGLE*™

Waggle can supplement your *Into Math* instruction by providing adaptive, targeted student practice.

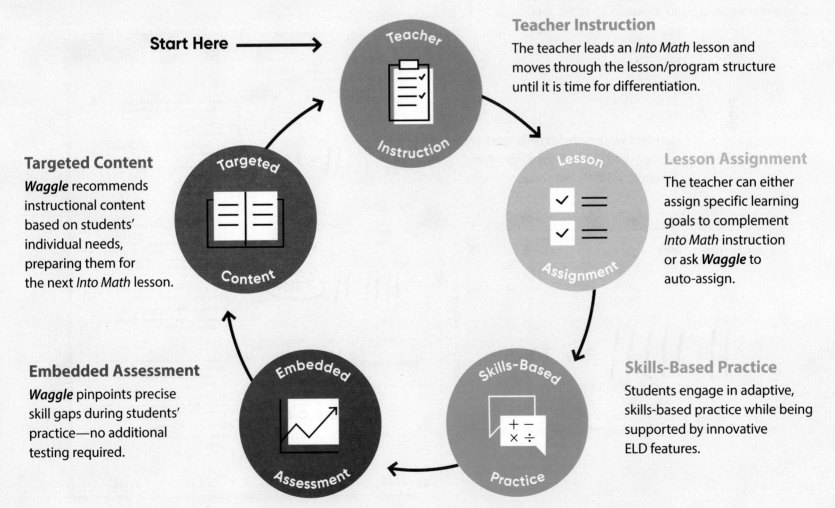

Start Here →

Teacher Instruction

The teacher leads an *Into Math* lesson and moves through the lesson/program structure until it is time for differentiation.

Lesson Assignment

The teacher can either assign specific learning goals to complement *Into Math* instruction or ask *Waggle* to auto-assign.

Skills-Based Practice

Students engage in adaptive, skills-based practice while being supported by innovative ELD features.

Embedded Assessment

Waggle pinpoints precise skill gaps during students' practice—no additional testing required.

Targeted Content

Waggle recommends instructional content based on students' individual needs, preparing them for the next *Into Math* lesson.

Teacher Support

Supporting Best Practices

Into Math classrooms maximize student growth by providing teachers with content designed around research-based, effective teaching practices, such as those described in *Principles to Actions* (NCTM, 2014).[1]

- Establish mathematics goals to focus learning.
- Implement tasks that promote reasoning and problem solving.
- Use and connect mathematical representations.
- Facilitate meaningful mathematical discourse.
- Pose purposeful questions.
- Build procedural fluency from conceptual understanding.
- Support productive struggle in learning mathematics.
- Elicit and use evidence of student thinking.

---

1) National Council of Teachers of Mathematics, *Principles to Actions: Ensuring Mathematical Success for All* (Reston, VA: NCTM, 2014).

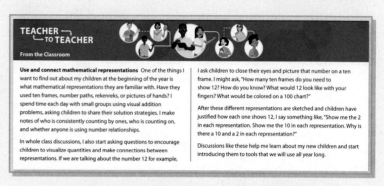

TEACHER → TO TEACHER
From the Classroom

Use and connect mathematical representations One of the things I want to find out about my children at the beginning of the year is what mathematical representations they are familiar with. Have they used ten frames, number paths, rekenreks, or pictures of hands? I spend time each day with small groups using visual addition problems, asking children to share their solution strategies. I make notes of who is consistently counting by ones, who is counting on, and whether anyone is using number relationships.

In whole class discussions, I also start asking questions to encourage children to visualize quantities and make connections between representations. If we are talking about the number 12 for example,

I ask children to close their eyes and picture that number on a ten frame. I might ask, "How many ten frames do you need to show 12? How do you know? What would 12 look like with your fingers? What would be colored on a 100 chart?"

After these different representations are sketched and children have justified how each one shows 12, I say something like, "Show me the 2 in each representation. Show me the 10 in each representation. Why is there a 10 and a 2 in each representation?"

Discussions like these help me learn about my new children and start introducing them to tools that we will use all year long.

Teacher to Teacher tips, aligned to the NCTM Effective Mathematics Teaching Practices, were written by educators for educators.

Student work samples help teachers understand student thinking behind possible solution pathways.

Show Adding Tens Strategy 1

|| ||||| = 7 tens

Spark Your Learning • Student Samples

During the *Spark Your Learning,* listen and watch for strategies children use. See samples of student work on this page.

Show Adding Tens Strategy 1

|| ||||| = 7 tens

If children . . . draw lines to show the starting number and then draw more lines to show the number of tens they tossed, they demonstrate they can make an accurate visual model. By including the sum, these children also demonstrate an understanding of adding tens.

Have these children . . . share their work with the class. **Ask:**

- How does drawing a visual model help you understand the problem?

Show Combined Group Strategy 2

|||||| (7 tens)

If children . . . toss a 5 and draw lines to show 7 tens and indicate the value by writing the number, they may have shown the solution correctly, but the model does not match the action of the problem. To help children learn how to make effective visual models, guide them to show the action in the problem.

Activate prior knowledge . . . by having these children draw another visual model. **Ask:**

- What is the action in the problem?
- How can you draw the tens to show you are adding them together?

COMMON ERROR: Shows Ones not Tens

|| ooooo

If children . . . show the starting number, but then show the number they tossed as ones rather than tens, they did not understand adding tens and more tens.

Then intervene . . . by reviewing concrete and visual models of tens with the children. Have them toss the number cube again. **Ask:**

- What number did you toss?
- How many tens do you add to the starting number?

349D Module 12

Carefully crafted tasks, student-centered learning, small groups, and hands-on manipulatives play important roles in an *Into Math* classroom. The *Into Math* Teacher Edition contains point-of-use support to help teachers facilitate learning and implement research-based best practices into their instruction.

Every module includes a professional learning video that features a teacher or HMH author working with real students who are engaging with actual content from the program. The videos include modeling and discussion of effective teaching practices and also feature the Language Routines and Talk Moves strategies.

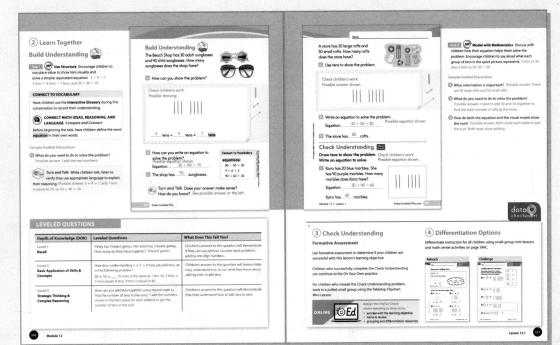

Leveled Questions and Sample Guided Instruction features help teachers ask questions that facilitate student understanding without giving away the answer.

Empowering Teachers

Into Math is designed to provide opportunities for each and every student to grow. Formative assessment and effective differentiation are critical to student success. However, care must be taken not to turn classrooms into unintentional tracking systems, which often create gates instead of gateways. Access to effective teaching and learning, a high-quality curriculum, and high expectations promote equitable math classrooms.

Professional Learning Cards help teachers effectively implement the Talk Moves and Language Routines, ensuring student reasoning and discourse play a key role in instruction.

Talk Moves

- Adding On
- Reasoning
- Repeating
- Revoicing
- Turn and Talk
- Waiting

Language Routines

- Three Reads
- Critique, Correct, and Clarify
- Stronger and Clearer Each Time
- Compare and Connect

Math Solutions professional learning publications, available to enhance your professional library, are referenced in the *Into Math* Teacher Edition.

Matthew R. Larson, PhD
Past President, National Council
of Teachers of Mathematics
Lincoln Public Schools
Lincoln, Nebraska
Math Solutions Senior Fellow

Ensuring Access and Equity

Access

Access and equity are a guiding principle of effective mathematics programs in which each and every student has access to effective instruction, high expectations, high-quality curriculum, and the support necessary to learn mathematics at a deep level (NCTM, 2014). *Into Math* provides the structure and resources needed to effectively differentiate instruction and support student learning.

The *Into Math* curriculum is rigorous and supports students' conceptual understanding, procedural fluency, and reasoning and problem-solving abilities through an intentional lesson and module design. *Into Math*'s frequent and embedded data checkpoints—linked to targeted instructional supports in print, digital, small-group, and math center options—are designed to ensure that each and every student has access to *Into Math*'s high-quality curriculum.

Equitable Instructional Practices

Mathematics teaching involves more than helping students acquire concepts and skills; it also includes supporting students in coming to see themselves as capable of learning, participating in, and becoming users of mathematics. Implementing equitable instructional practices can improve students' classroom experience, learning outcomes, and disposition toward mathematics.

The mathematics teaching practices included in *Into Math* provide an instructional framework for cultivating students' confidence and belief in their ability to learn and use mathematics. For example, the tasks in Spark Your Learning are designed as "low-floor/high-ceiling" tasks that all students can access but that can also be extended to provide challenge. These tasks motivate learning, focus on building students' conceptual understanding to help ensure procedural fluency, encourage the use of multiple representations, and help students develop a positive disposition toward mathematics and themselves as learners.

Similarly, Turn and Talk prompts position students as mathematically competent and capable of sharing their thinking and participating in mathematical arguments. Through discourse, students realize that their thinking serves an important role in learning mathematics and cultivate their confidence as learners[1], which, in turn, improves the learning outcomes of each and every student.

 Turn and Talk How does knowing $6 + 4 = 10$ help you find $10 - 6 = \blacksquare$? Explain.

---

1) D. Huinker & V. Bill, *Taking Action: Implementing Effective Mathematics Teaching Practices in K–Grade 5*, ed. M. S. Smith (Reston, VA: NCTM, 2017).

Teacher Support

Building a Culture of Professional Growth

A blend of in-person and online support with Math Solutions® coaches fosters a culture of professional growth and inspires a culture of math achievement with every student, in every classroom, every day.

Coaches from Math Solutions® will work side by side with teachers to develop instructional practices that promote reasoning and problem-solving skills. Our goal is to support teachers as they create learning environments where students are encouraged to become fearless problem solvers.

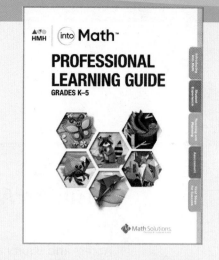

Math Solutions® Partner with Math Solutions® to deepen your practice to meet the learning needs of each and every student and effectively maneuver the challenges you face in your classroom every day.

During the *Getting Started with Into Math* session, teachers receive a Professional Learning Guide. The Professional Learning Guide is also available on Ed: Your Friend in Learning.

Getting Started Modules can be accessed anywhere and anytime on Ed: Your Friend in Learning.

The single greatest determinant for success in a classroom is the teacher. Math Solutions® coaches partner with you as you make critical decisions that impact student learning.

Weston Kieschnick
Associate Partner
International Center for
Leadership in Education
Littleton, Colorado

Blended Learning That Works

Purposeful Technology Use + Old-School Wisdom

We know that digital tools and future-focused learning environments are critical when preparing our students for the real world. But what about the tried-and-true teaching strategies that have always driven real and measurable learning? Where do these fit in?

The Bold School Framework for Strategic Blended Learning™ puts teachers back into the digital learning equation. Its practical yet powerful approach shows how purposeful technology use combined with old-school wisdom can elevate instruction and enhance learning.

Effective 21st-century learning blends sound pedagogical practices with digital elements to create engaging rigorous and relevant experiences. As educators, we are accountable for the learning outcomes and career readiness of our students. Technology and digital tools, when implemented strategically to enhance—not replace—sound pedagogy, create effective and efficient blended learning experiences for students. Here's how it works.

	Bold School Framework for Strategic Blended Learning™
Step 1	Identify Desired Academic Outcome(s)
Step 2	Select a Goal-Aligned Instructional Strategy That *Works*
Step 3	Choose Digital Tool(s)
Step 4	Plan Blended Instruction
Step 5	Self-Assess Your Plans and Progress with a Framework

The goal of using technology isn't just to use technology—it's student achievement. We must approach blended learning with greater intention than just "What am I going to do with (insert tech tool here) today?" With this mindset, every teacher can support students through the power of digital learning.

Fostering Learning Mindsets

Through a partnership with Mindset Works®, *Into Math* incorporates the latest research, strategies, and practices to build a community of resilient, curious learners.

- Introduce the learning mindsets—growth mindset, relevance, belonging, and purpose—to help students better understand their self perception and attitudes toward learning.
- Establish the tenets of growth mindset, so that each student understands that he or she has the capacity to learn and grow.
- Target the research-based stances and skills that are key to student agency, engagement, and academic success.

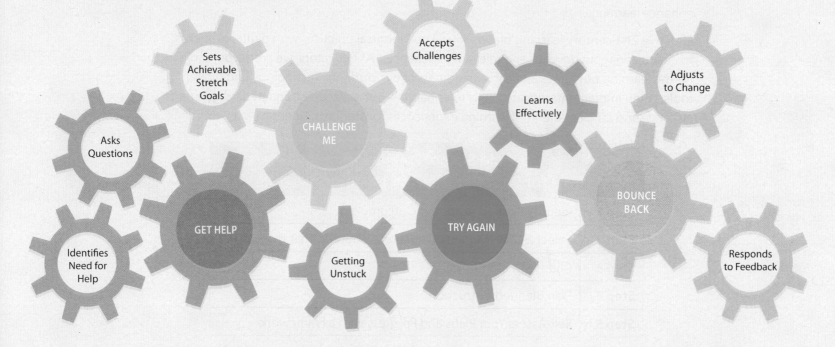

Connect with Families and Community

Engaging with families and the community is critical to student success in school. *Into Math* provides resources to help teachers interact with families throughout the school year.

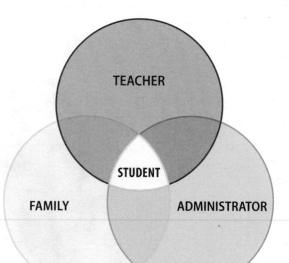

- **Math on the Spot** video tutorials provide instruction of the math concepts covered and allow for family involvement in their child's learning. The write-in format of the Student Edition gives families a front-row seat to their child's thinking and progress over time, encouraging a strong home–school connection.
- **School Home Letters** inform families about the skills, strategies, and topics students are encountering at school, extending rich dialogue beyond the classroom.

David Dockterman, EdD
Lecturer, Harvard Graduate
School of Education
Cambridge, Massachusetts

Understanding Mindset

Into Math fosters a growth mindset by explicitly teaching students that intelligence is not a fixed trait, but rather hard work and determination are crucial factors in raising academic achievement. Students often believe that their ability to excel in mathematics is fixed. Carol Dweck, a psychologist at Stanford University and leading researcher in student motivation and development, highlights the academic benefits of adopting a "growth" mindset rather than a "fixed" mindset.

Growth Mindset

Growth mindset is the idea that intelligence and abilities can be developed through dedication and work. "This view creates a drive towards learning and a resilience that is essential for great accomplishment. Virtually all great people have had these qualities."[1] Instruction and classroom community can foster a growth mindset by explicitly teaching that effort has a meaningful impact on learning.[2] Students with a growth mindset believe:

- Practice and effort are key elements in developing intelligence.
- Persistence and perseverance are important factors in triumphing over setbacks and failures.
- Mistakes and struggle are part of the learning process.

Fixed Mindset

Students who have a fixed mindset believe that intelligence and abilities are fixed traits that cannot be developed. Students who view their intelligence as fixed from birth are more likely to experience decreased confidence and performance when faced with challenges.[3] Students with a fixed mindset

- believe intelligence is a fixed quantity that you either possess or lack,
- put in less effort and give up easily, and
- fear failure and are less likely to take risks.

Teaching Growth Mindset

Feedback and classroom discourse can have a lasting impact on how students view intelligence.[4] By adopting a growth mindset and productive learning strategies, students are more likely to step up to challenges and persevere through and bounce back from adversity. Use the following strategies:

- Teach that intelligence and abilities are developed.
- Praise students' efforts and strategies rather than their intelligence.
- Use "mistakes" or incorrect answers as teachable moments.

1) C. Dweck, *Mindset: The New Psychology of Success.* (New York, NY: Penguin Random House, 2006).

2) L.S. Blackwell, K.H. Trzesniewski, C.S. Dweck, "Theories of Intelligence Predict Achievement Across an Adolescent Transition: A Longitudinal Study and an Intervention," *Child Development* 78, no. 1 (January-February 2007): 246–263.

3) Blackwell, Trzesniewski, Dweck, "Theories of Intelligence . . . ," 246–263.

4) M. Malmivuori, "Affect and Self-Regulation," *Educational Studies in Mathematics* 63, no. 2 (October 2006): 149–164.

Unpacking Math Standards

Into Math is built on a carefully crafted Learning Spine based on the Mathematics Standards, with a coherent progression from kindergarten through algebra and beyond. The *Into Math* system allows for easy access forward or backward across the K–12 Mathematical Progressions, providing teachers with the tools to navigate prerequisite and follow-on concepts and skills.

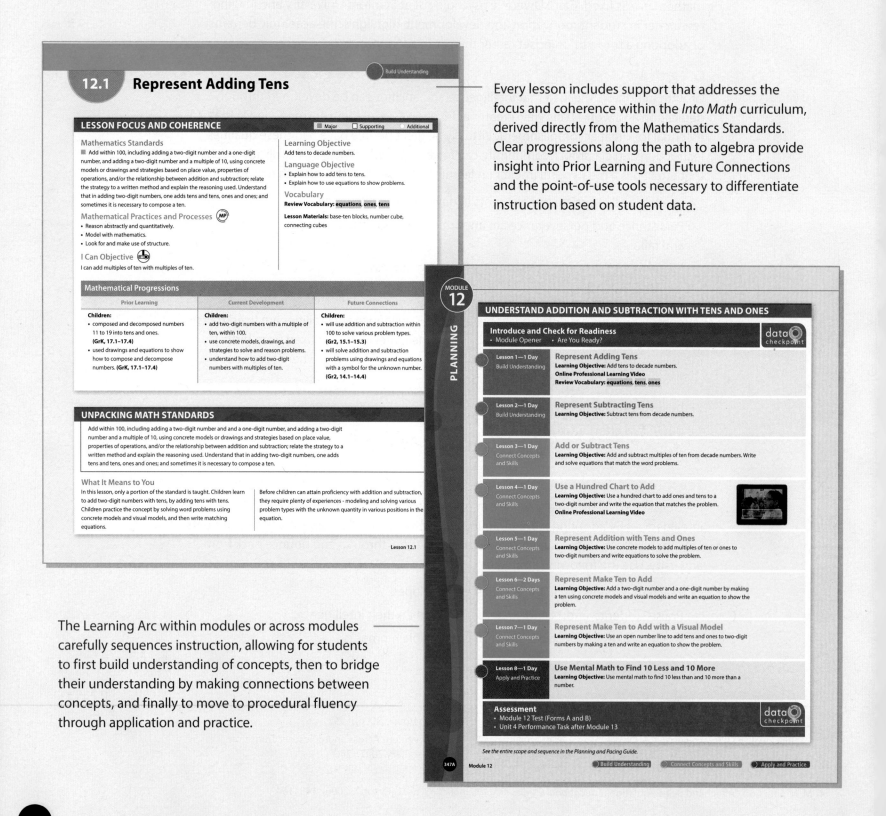

Every lesson includes support that addresses the focus and coherence within the *Into Math* curriculum, derived directly from the Mathematics Standards. Clear progressions along the path to algebra provide insight into Prior Learning and Future Connections and the point-of-use tools necessary to differentiate instruction based on student data.

The Learning Arc within modules or across modules carefully sequences instruction, allowing for students to first build understanding of concepts, then to bridge their understanding by making connections between concepts, and finally to move to procedural fluency through application and practice.

Timothy D. Kanold, PhD
Mathematics Educator
Chicago, Illinois

Progressions and Algebra Readiness

Algebra Readiness in 2020 and Beyond

Algebra as a course of study today is integrated around four progressions of elementary and middle school content leading to the algebra course: Number and Operations, Operations and Algebraic Thinking, Statistics and Probability, and Functions.

	Grades K–5	Grades 6–7	Grade 8 and Algebra
1	Number and Operations Base Ten	The Number System Extended	Expand to Numbers Not Rational
2	Operations and Algebraic Thinking	Writing, Interpreting, and Using Expressions and Equations	Modeling with and Solving Linear Equations and Systems
3	Measurement and Data	Statistics and Probability Variability, Inferences, and Chance	Statistics and Probability Bivariate Data, Lines of Best Fit
4	Number and Operations Fractions	Analyze and Apply Ratios and Proportional Relationships	Functions Define, Evaluate, and Compare

The Operations and Algebraic Thinking progression strand is unique to the K–5 preparation for the algebra readiness curriculum.

The Operations and Algebraic Thinking Progression

Operations and Algebraic Thinking is a K–5 progression that feeds directly into the middle school progression for linear expressions and equations.

At grade levels K–2, this progression focuses on counting, place value, and addition and subtraction of whole numbers. The emphasis is on representing and solving Add To, Take From, Put Together/Take Apart, and Compare problem situations for addition and subtraction. This work will help students to "see" multiplication as groups of objects and as represented by a rectangular array or model in Grades 3–5. Conceptual building blocks are developed for the eventual multiplication of whole numbers.

At grade levels 3–5, this progression expands into the conceptual student understanding needed for students to "see" patterns, properties, and expressions in problem situations—the early foundations of what will become known as algebra. These progressions include multiplication and division problem situations with equal groups, arrays, area, and comparisons. Third graders focus on fluency when multiplying and dividing within 100, fourth graders analyze shape and number patterns, and fifth graders use problem situations that allow them to both write and interpret numerical expressions based on earlier student work with whole numbers.

Teacher Support

Supporting Intervention Needs

Into Math provides the supports teachers need to ensure each and every student succeeds. Data informs teachers' use of differentiated Small-Group and Math Center options in every lesson. *Into Math* includes intervention content for use in a core classroom.

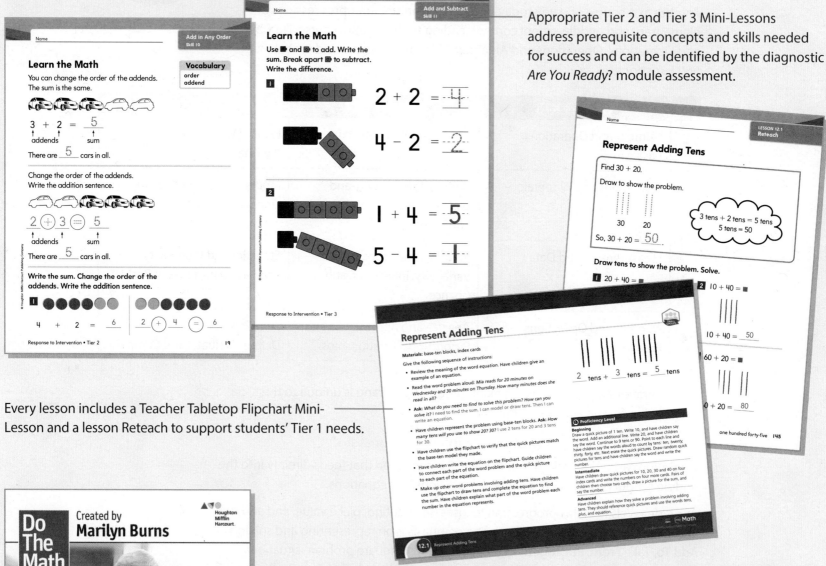

Appropriate Tier 2 and Tier 3 Mini-Lessons address prerequisite concepts and skills needed for success and can be identified by the diagnostic *Are You Ready?* module assessment.

Every lesson includes a Teacher Tabletop Flipchart Mini-Lesson and a lesson Reteach to support students' Tier 1 needs.

HMH also offers robust Intervention Solutions for students who need targeted and intensive intervention. Developed by Marilyn Burns, *Do the Math* has thirteen modules that are organized into four topics—Addition and Subtraction, Multiplication, Division, and Fractions. These modules provide carefully scaffolded instruction to build conceptual understanding and develop numerical reasoning. See pages PG72–PG73.

- grades 1 and up
- can be used during core instruction or in a separate instruction block
- effective and easily managed instruction with embedded assessments
- includes digital resources
- six weeks of 30-minute lessons in each module

Foundational Research

Hattie, J., Fisher, D., & Frey, N. (2017). *Visible Learning for Mathematics: What Works Best to Optimize Student Learning.* Thousand Oaks, CA: Corwin.

National Council of Teachers of Mathematics (NCTM). (2014). *Principles to Actions: Ensuring Mathematical Success for All.* Reston, VA: NCTM.

National Research Council. Kilpatrick, J., Swafford, J., & Findell, B. (Eds.), (2001). *Adding It Up: Helping Children Learn Mathematics.* Washington, DC: National Academy Press.

National Research Council. (2005). *How Students Learn: Mathematics in the Classroom.* Washington, DC: National Academies Press.

Schielack, J., Charles, R., Clements, D., Duckett, P., Fennell, F. (Skip)., Lewandowski, S., Trevino, E., Zbiek, R.M., (2006). *Curriculum Focal Points for Prekindergarten through Grade 8 Mathematics.* Reston, VA: NCTM.

Curriculum Design and Standards

Common Core Standards Writing Team. (2013). *Progressions for the Common Core State Standards Mathematics*

National Board for Professional Teaching Standards. (2010, preface rev. 2015, 2016). *Mathematics Standards for Teachers of Students Ages 11–18+.* Arlington, VA: National Board for Professional Teaching Standards.

National Governors Association Center for Best Practices, Council of Chief State School Officers. (2012). *Common Core State Standards: K-8 Publisher's Criteria for the Common Core State Standards for Mathematics.* Washington, DC: National Governors Association Center for Best Practices, Council of Chief State School Officers.

Mathematics Knowledge for Teaching

Ball, D.L., Thames, M. H., & Phelps, G. (2008). Content knowledge for Teaching: What Makes It Special?. *Journal of Teacher Education, 59(5),* 389-407.

Chapin, S. H., O'Connor, C., & Anderson, N. C. (2013). *Classroom Discussions in Math: A Teacher's Guide for Using Talk Moves to Support the Common Core and more, Grades K-6* (3rd edition). Sausalito, CA: Math Solutions.

Chapin, S .H., & Johnson, A. (2000). *Math Matters: Understanding the Math You Teach. Grades K-6.* Sausalito, CA: Math Solutions.

Dean, C.B., Hubbell, E.R., Pitler, H., & Stone, B.J. (2nd ed., 2012). *Classroom Instruction that Works: Research-Based Strategies for Increasing Student Achievement.* Alexandria, VA: Association for Supervision and Curriculum Development.

Dixon, J.K., Nolan, E.C., Adams, T.L., Brooks, L.A., Howse, T.D. (2016). *Making Sense of Mathematics for Teaching Grades K-2.* Bloomington, IN: Solution Tree Press.

Dixon, J.K., Nolan, E.C., Adams, T.L., Tobias, J.M., Barmoha, G. (2016). *Making Sense of Mathematics for Teaching Grades 3-5.* Bloomington, IN: Solution Tree Press.

Hill, H. C., Ball, D. L., & Schilling, S. G. (2008). Unpacking Pedagogical Content Knowledge: Conceptualizing and Measuring Teachers' Topic-Specific Knowledge of Students. *Journal for Research in Mathematics Education, 39(4),* 372-400.

Huinker, D., & Bill, V. Smith, M.S. (Ed), (2017). *Taking Action: Implementing Effective Mathematics Teaching Practices in K-Grade 5.* Reston VA: NCTM.

Ma, L. (2nd ed., 2010). *Knowing and Teaching Elementary Mathematics: Teachers' Understanding of Fundamental Mathematics in China and the United States.* New York, NY: Routledge.

Nolan, E.C., Dixon, J.K., Roy, G.J., Andreasen, J.B. (2016). *Making Sense of Mathematics for Teaching Grades 6-8.* Bloomington, IN: Solution Tree Press.

Nolan, E.C., Dixon, J.K., Safi, F., Haciomeroglu, E.S. (2016). *Making Sense of Mathematics for Teaching High School.* Bloomington, IN: Solution Tree Press.

Petersen, J. (2013). *Math Games for Number and Operations and Algebraic Thinking: Games to Support Independent Practice in Math Workshops and More, Grades K-5.* Sausalito, CA: Math Solutions.

Schoenfeld, A. H. (2014). What Makes for Powerful Classrooms, and How Can We Support Teachers in Creating Them? A Story of Research and Practice, Productively Intertwined. *Educational Researcher, 43(8),* 404-412.

Shulman, L. S. (1986/2013). Those Who Understand: Knowledge Growth in Teaching. *The Journal of Education,* 193(3), 1-11.

Smith, M.S., & Stein, M.K. (2nd ed., 2018). *Five Practices for Orchestrating Productive Mathematical Discussion.* Thousand Oaks, CA: Corwin.

Steele, M., & Raith, M.L. Smith, M.S. (Ed), (2017). *Taking Action: Implementing Effective Mathematics Teaching Practices in Grades 6-8.* Reston VA: NCTM.

Differentiation

Dacey, L., Lynch, J. B., & Salemi, R. E. (2013). *How to Differentiate Your Math Instruction: Lessons, Ideas, and Videos with Common Core Support.* Sausalito, CA: Math Solutions.

Small, M. (3rd ed., 2017). *Good Questions: Great Ways to Differentiate Mathematics Instruction in the Standards-Based Classroom.* New York, NY: Teachers College Press.

English Language Learners

Council of the Great City Schools. (2014). *A Framework for Raising Expectations and Instructional Rigor for English Language Learners.*

National Council of Teachers of Mathematics (NCTM). Civil, M., & Turner, E. (Eds), (2014). *The Common Core State Standards in Mathematics for English Language Learners: Grades K-8.* Alexandria, VA: TESOL Press.

Zwiers, J., Dieckmann, J., Rutherford-Quach, S., Daro, V., Skarin, R., Weiss, S., & Malamut, J. (2017). *Principles for the Design of Mathematics Curricula: Promoting Language and Content Development.* Stanford, CA: Stanford University.

Continued on next page →

Professional Learning References

Equity

Aguirre, J., Mayfield-Ingram, K., Martin, D. (2013). *The Impact of Identity in K-8 Mathematics: Rethinking Equity-Based Practices.* Reston, VA: The National Council of Teachers of Mathematics.

Boaler, J., & Staples, M. (2008). Creating Mathematical Futures through an Equitable Teaching Approach: The Case of Railside School. *Teachers College Record,* 110(3), 608-645.

Flores, A. (2007). Examining Disparities in Mathematics Education: Achievement Gap or Opportunity Gap?. *High School Journal,* 91(1), 29-42.

Howard, T. C. (2010). *Why Race and Culture Matter in Schools: Closing the Achievement Gap in America's Classrooms* (2009). New York, NY: Teachers College Press.

Larson, M. R., & Andrews, D. (2015). One District's Journey to Promote Access and Equity. *New England Mathematics Journal,* XLVII, 31-40.

Leinwand, S. (2009). *Accessible Mathematics: 10 Instructional Shifts that Raise Student Achievement.* Portsmouth, NH: Heinemann.

Learning Mindset

Boaler, Jo (2016). *Mathematical Mindsets: Unleashing Students' Potential through Creative Math, Inspiring Messages and Innovative Teaching.* San Francisco, CA: Jossey-Bass.

Dockterman, D., & Blackwell, L. (2014). Growth Mindset in Context: Content and Culture Matter Too. *International Center for Leadership in Education,* 1-4.

Dweck, C. S. (2006). *Mindset: The New Psychology of Success.* New York, N.Y.: Penguin Random House.

Digital Learning Environment

Delgado, A.J., Wardlow, L., McKnight, K., & O'Malley, K. (2015). Educational Technology: A Review of the Integration, Resources, and Effectiveness of Technology in K-12 Classrooms. *Journal of Information Technology Education: Research,* 14, 397-416.

Imbriale, R. (2013). Blended Learning. *Principal Leadership,* 13(6), 30-34.

Kieschnick, W. (2017). International Center forLeadership in Education, Inc. *Bold School: Old School Wisdom + New School Technologies = Blended Learning that Works.* Rexford, NY.

Mayer, R. E. (2013). Multimedia Learning. In *Educational Psychology Handbook: International Guide to Student Achievement,* J. Hattie & E. Anderman (Eds.). 396-398. New York, N.Y.: Routledge.

Modern Teacher. (2016). *Digital Convergence: The Path Toward the K-12 Modern Learning Environment.* Denver, CO: Modern Teacher.

Public Impact. (2013). *A Better Blend: A Vision for Boosting Student Outcomes with Digital Learning.* Chapel Hill, NC: Public Impact.

Ross, S.M., Morrison, G.R., & Lowther, D.L. (2010). Educational Technology Research Past and Present: Balancing Rigor and Relevance to Impact School Learning. *Contemporary Educational Technology,* 1(1), 17-35.

Schneider, M.C., Egan, K.L., & Julian, M.W. (2013). Classroom Assessment in the Context of High-Stakes Testing. In *SAGE Handbook of Research on Classroom Assessment,* J. McMillan (Ed.). 55-70. Thousand Oaks, CA: SAGE.

U.S. Department of Education, Office of Planning, Evaluation, and Policy Development. (2009). *Evaluation of Evidence-Based Practices in Online Learning: A Meta-Analysis and Review of Online Learning Studies.* Washington, DC: U.S. Department of Education.

Assessment, Data, & Reports

Black, P., & Wiliam, D. (1998). Inside the Black Box: Raising Standards through Classroom Assessment. *Phi Delta Kappan,* 80(2), 139-144.

Popham, W. J. (8th ed., 2018). *Classroom Assessment: What Teachers Need to Know.* London: Pearson.

Stiggins, R. (2008). *Assessment Manifesto: A Call for the Development of Balanced Assessment Systems.* Portland, OR: ETS Assessment Training Institute.

Professional Learning

Darling-Hammond, L., Wei, R.C., Andree, A., Richardson, N., & Orphanos, S. (2009). *Professional Learning in the Learning Profession: A Status Report on Teacher Development in the United States and Abroad.* Oxford, OH: National Staff Development Council.

Dixon, J. K., Egendoerfer, L. A., & Clements, T. (2009). Do They Really Need to Raise Their Hands? Challenging a Traditional Social Norm in a Second Grade Mathematics Classroom. *Teaching and Teacher Education,* 25(8), 1067-1076.

Garet, M.S., Porter, A.C., Desimone, L., Birman, B.F., & Yoon, K.S. (2001). What Makes Professional Development Effective? Results from a National Sample of Teachers. *American Educational Research Journal,* 38(4), 915-945.

Hargreaves, A., & Fullan, M. (2013). The Power of Professional Capital: With an Investment in Collaboration, Teachers become Nation Builders. *Journal of Staff Development,* 34(3), 36-39.

Kanold, T.D., Kanold-McIntyre, J., Larson, M.R., Barnes, B., Schuhl, S., & Toncheff, M. (2018). *Mathematics Instruction & Tasks in a PLC at Work.* Bloomington, IN: Solution Tree Press.

Kelemanik, G., Lucenta, A., & Janssen Creighton, S. (2016). *Routines for Reasoning: Fostering the Mathematical Practices in All Students.* Portsmouth, NH: Heinemann.

Knight, J. (2007). *Instructional Coaching: A Partnership Approach to Improving Instruction.* Thousand Oaks, CA: Corwin.

Leinwand, S. (2nd ed., 2012) *Sensible Mathematics.* Portsmouth, NH: Heinemann.

Sweeney, D. (2011) *Student-Centered Coaching.* Thousand Oaks, CA: Corwin Press.

Notes & Reflections

Pacing Guide

Lesson	Mathematics Standards, Grade 1	Pacing
Unit 1 WAYS TO ADD AND SUBTRACT		
Module 1: Addition Strategies		
Lesson 1.1 Represent Addition	■ Use addition and subtraction within 20 to solve word problems involving situations of adding to, taking from, putting together, taking apart, and comparing, with unknowns in all positions, e.g., by using objects, drawings, and equations with a symbol for the unknown number to represent the problem.	1 day
Lesson 1.2 Count On	■ Relate counting to addition and subtraction (e.g., by counting on 2 to add 2).	2 days
Lesson 1.3 Add 10 and More	■ Add and subtract within 20, demonstrating fluency for addition and subtraction within 10. Use strategies such as counting on; making ten (e.g., $8 + 6 = 8 + 2 + 4 = 10 + 4 = 14$); decomposing a number leading to a ten (e.g., $13 - 4 = 13 - 3 - 1 = 10 - 1 = 9$); using the relationship between addition and subtraction (e.g., knowing that $8 + 4 = 12$, one knows $12 - 8 = 4$); and creating equivalent but easier or known sums (e.g., adding $6 + 7$ by creating the known equivalent $6 + 6 + 1 = 12 + 1 = 13$).	1 day
Lesson 1.4 Make a 10 to Add	■ Add and subtract within 20, demonstrating fluency for addition and subtraction within 10. Use strategies such as counting on; making ten (e.g., $8 + 6 = 8 + 2 + 4 = 10 + 4 = 14$); decomposing a number leading to a ten (e.g., $13 - 4 = 13 - 3 - 1 = 10 - 1 = 9$); using the relationship between addition and subtraction (e.g., knowing that $8 + 4 = 12$, one knows $12 - 8 = 4$); and creating equivalent but easier or known sums (e.g., adding $6 + 7$ by creating the known equivalent $6 + 6 + 1 = 12 + 1 = 13$).	2 days
Lesson 1.5 Add Doubles	■ Add and subtract within 20, demonstrating fluency for addition and subtraction within 10. Use strategies such as counting on; making ten (e.g., $8 + 6 = 8 + 2 + 4 = 10 + 4 = 14$); decomposing a number leading to a ten (e.g., $13 - 4 = 13 - 3 - 1 = 10 - 1 = 9$); using the relationship between addition and subtraction (e.g., knowing that $8 + 4 = 12$, one knows $12 - 8 = 4$); and creating equivalent but easier or known sums (e.g., adding $6 + 7$ by creating the known equivalent $6 + 6 + 1 = 12 + 1 = 13$).	1 day
Lesson 1.6 Use Known Sums to Add	■ Add and subtract within 20, demonstrating fluency for addition and subtraction within 10. Use strategies such as counting on; making ten (e.g., $8 + 6 = 8 + 2 + 4 = 10 + 4 = 14$); decomposing a number leading to a ten (e.g., $13 - 4 = 13 - 3 - 1 = 10 - 1 = 9$); using the relationship between addition and subtraction (e.g., knowing that $8 + 4 = 12$, one knows $12 - 8 = 4$); and creating equivalent but easier or known sums (e.g., adding $6 + 7$ by creating the known equivalent $6 + 6 + 1 = 12 + 1 = 13$).	1 day

Major
Supporting
Additional

In addition to the core instructional pacing, HMH recommends the following:
• 3 days per year for the HMH Into Math Growth Measure powered by Math Inventory
• 2 days per module for the Module Opener, Are You Ready?, Module Review, and Module Test
• 1 day per unit for the Performance Task
Using these recommendations, the total pacing for Grade 1 is 162 days.

Lesson	Mathematics Standards, Grade 1	Pacing
○ Lesson 1.7 Choose a Strategy to Add	■ Use addition and subtraction within 20 to solve word problems involving situations of adding to, taking from, putting together, taking apart, and comparing, with unknowns in all positions, e.g., by using objects, drawings, and equations with a symbol for the unknown number to represent the problem. ■ Add and subtract within 20, demonstrating fluency for addition and subtraction within 10. Use strategies such as counting on; making ten (e.g., $8 + 6 = 8 + 2 + 4 = 10 + 4 = 14$); decomposing a number leading to a ten (e.g., $13 - 4 = 13 - 3 - 1 = 10 - 1 = 9$); using the relationship between addition and subtraction (e.g., knowing that $8 + 4 = 12$, one knows $12 - 8 = 4$); and creating equivalent but easier or known sums (e.g., adding $6 + 7$ by creating the known equivalent $6 + 6 + 1 = 12 + 1 = 13$).	2 days

Module 2: Subtraction Strategies

Lesson	Mathematics Standards, Grade 1	Pacing
○ Lesson 2.1 Represent Subtraction	■ Use addition and subtraction within 20 to solve word problems involving situations of adding to, taking from, putting together, taking apart, and comparing, with unknowns in all positions, e.g., by using objects, drawings, and equations with a symbol for the unknown number to represent the problem.	1 day
○ Lesson 2.2 Count Back	■ Relate counting to addition and subtraction (e.g., by counting on 2 to add 2).	2 days
○ Lesson 2.3 Count On to Subtract	■ Relate counting to addition and subtraction (e.g., by counting on 2 to add 2).	1 day
○ Lesson 2.4 Add to Subtract	■ Understand subtraction as an unknown-addend problem. ■ Add and subtract within 20, demonstrating fluency for addition and subtraction within 10. Use strategies such as counting on; making ten (e.g., $8 + 6 = 8 + 2 + 4 = 10 + 4 = 14$); decomposing a number leading to a ten (e.g., $13 - 4 = 13 - 3 - 1 = 10 - 1 = 9$); using the relationship between addition and subtraction (e.g., knowing that $8 + 4 = 12$, one knows $12 - 8 = 4$); and creating equivalent but easier or known sums (e.g., adding $6 + 7$ by creating the known equivalent $6 + 6 + 1 = 12 + 1 = 13$). ■ Determine the unknown whole number in an addition or subtraction equation relating to three whole numbers.	1 day
○ Lesson 2.5 Use 10 to Subtract	■ Add and subtract within 20, demonstrating fluency for addition and subtraction within 10. Use strategies such as counting on; making ten (e.g., $8 + 6 = 8 + 2 + 4 = 10 + 4 = 14$); decomposing a number leading to a ten (e.g., $13 - 4 = 13 - 3 - 1 = 10 - 1 = 9$); using the relationship between addition and subtraction (e.g., knowing that $8 + 4 = 12$, one knows $12 - 8 = 4$); and creating equivalent but easier or known sums (e.g., adding $6 + 7$ by creating the known equivalent $6 + 6 + 1 = 12 + 1 = 13$).	2 days

Module continued on next page →

Pacing Guide

Lesson	Mathematics Standards, Grade 1	Pacing
Module 2: Subtraction Strategies		
Lesson 2.6 Choose a Strategy to Subtract	■ Use addition and subtraction within 20 to solve word problems involving situations of adding to, taking from, putting together, taking apart, and comparing, with unknowns in all positions, e.g., by using objects, drawings, and equations with a symbol for the unknown number to represent the problem. ■ Add and subtract within 20, demonstrating fluency for addition and subtraction within 10. Use strategies such as counting on; making ten (e.g., $8 + 6 = 8 + 2 + 4 = 10 + 4 = 14$); decomposing a number leading to a ten (e.g., $13 - 4 = 13 - 3 - 1 = 10 - 1 = 9$); using the relationship between addition and subtraction (e.g., knowing that $8 + 4 = 12$, one knows $12 - 8 = 4$); and creating equivalent but easier or known sums (e.g., adding $6 + 7$ by creating the known equivalent $6 + 6 + 1 = 12 + 1 = 13$).	2 days
Module 3: Properties of Operations		
Lesson 3.1 Represent Addition in Any Order	■ Apply properties of operations as strategies to add and subtract.	1 day
Lesson 3.2 Add in Any Order	■ Apply properties of operations as strategies to add and subtract.	1 day
Lesson 3.3 Represent Addition of 3 Numbers	■ Apply properties of operations as strategies to add and subtract. ■ Solve word problems that call for addition of three whole numbers whose sum is less than or equal to 20, e.g., by using objects, drawings, and equations with a symbol for the unknown number to represent the problem.	1 day
Lesson 3.4 Add 3 Numbers	■ Apply properties of operations as strategies to add and subtract. ■ Solve word problems that call for addition of three whole numbers whose sum is less than or equal to 20, e.g., by using objects, drawings, and equations with a symbol for the unknown number to represent the problem.	1 day
Lesson 3.5 Add 3 Numbers to Solve Problems	■ Solve word problems that call for addition of three whole numbers whose sum is less than or equal to 20, e.g., by using objects, drawings, and equations with a symbol for the unknown number to represent the problem. ■ Apply properties of operations as strategies to add and subtract.	1 day
Lesson 3.6 Determine Equal and Not Equal	■ Understand the meaning of the equal sign and determine if equations involving addition and subtraction are true or false.	1 day
Lesson 3.7 Develop Fluency in Addition	■ Add and subtract within 20, demonstrating fluency for addition and subtraction within 10. Use strategies such as counting on; making ten (e.g., $8 + 6 = 8 + 2 + 4 = 10 + 4 = 14$); decomposing a number leading to a ten (e.g., $13 - 4 = 13 - 3 - 1 = 10 - 1 = 9$); using the relationship between addition and subtraction (e.g., knowing that $8 + 4 = 12$, one knows $12 - 8 = 4$); and creating equivalent but easier or known sums (e.g., adding $6 + 7$ by creating the known equivalent $6 + 6 + 1 = 12 + 1 = 13$).	1 day

Lesson	Mathematics Standards, Grade 1	Pacing
Module 4: Apply the Addition and Subtraction Relationship		
Lesson 4.1 Think Addition to Subtract	■ Understand subtraction as an unknown-addend problem. ■ Add and subtract within 20, demonstrating fluency for addition and subtraction within 10. Use strategies such as counting on; making ten (e.g., $8 + 6 = 8 + 2 + 4 = 10 + 4 = 14$); decomposing a number leading to a ten (e.g., $13 - 4 = 13 - 3 - 1 = 10 - 1 = 9$); using the relationship between addition and subtraction (e.g., knowing that $8 + 4 = 12$, one knows $12 - 8 = 4$); and creating equivalent but easier known sums (e.g., adding $6 + 7$ by creating the known equivalent $6 + 6 + 1 = 12 + 1 = 13$). ■ Determine the unknown whole number in an addition or subtraction equation relating to three whole numbers.	2 days
Lesson 4.2 Represent Related Facts	■ Add and subtract within 20, demonstrating fluency for addition and subtraction within 10. Use strategies such as counting on; making ten (e.g., $8 + 6 = 8 + 2 + 4 = 10 + 4 = 14$); decomposing a number leading to a ten (e.g., $13 - 4 = 13 - 3 - 1 = 10 - 1 = 9$); using the relationship between addition and subtraction (e.g., knowing that $8 + 4 = 12$, one knows $12 - 8 = 4$); and creating equivalent but easier known sums (e.g., adding $6 + 7$ by creating the known equivalent $6 + 6 + 1 = 12 + 1 = 13$).	1 day
Lesson 4.3 Identify Related Facts	■ Add and subtract within 20, demonstrating fluency for addition and subtraction within 10. Use strategies such as counting on; making ten (e.g., $8 + 6 = 8 + 2 + 4 = 10 + 4 = 14$); decomposing a number leading to a ten (e.g., $13 - 4 = 13 - 3 - 1 = 10 - 1 = 9$); using the relationship between addition and subtraction (e.g., knowing that $8 + 4 = 12$, one knows $12 - 8 = 4$); and creating equivalent but easier known sums (e.g., adding $6 + 7$ by creating the known equivalent $6 + 6 + 1 = 12 + 1 = 13$).	1 day
Lesson 4.4 Use Addition to Check Subtraction	■ Add and subtract within 20, demonstrating fluency for addition and subtraction within 10. Use strategies such as counting on; making ten (e.g., $8 + 6 = 8 + 2 + 4 = 10 + 4 = 14$); decomposing a number leading to a ten (e.g., $13 - 4 = 13 - 3 - 1 = 10 - 1 = 9$); using the relationship between addition and subtraction (e.g., knowing that $8 + 4 = 12$, one knows $12 - 8 = 4$); and creating equivalent but easier known sums (e.g., adding $6 + 7$ by creating the known equivalent $6 + 6 + 1 = 12 + 1 = 13$).	1 day
Lesson 4.5 Use Subtraction to Find an Unknown Addend	■ Determine the unknown whole number in an addition or subtraction equation relating to three whole numbers.	1 day
Lesson 4.6 Solve for the Unknown Addend	■ Use addition and subtraction within 20 to solve word problems involving situations of adding to, taking from, putting together, taking apart, and comparing, with unknowns in all positions, e.g., by using objects, drawings, and equations with a symbol for the unknown number to represent the problem. ■ Determine the unknown whole number in an addition or subtraction equation relating to three whole numbers.	1 day

Module continued on next page →

Pacing Guide

Build Understanding
Connect Concepts and Skills
Apply and Practice

Lesson	Mathematics Standards, Grade 1	Pacing
Module 4: Apply the Addition and Subtraction Relationship		
Lesson 4.7 Develop Fluency in Subtraction	Add and subtract within 20, demonstrating fluency for addition and subtraction within 10. Use strategies such as counting on; making ten (e.g., $8 + 6 = 8 + 2 + 4 = 10 + 4 = 14$); decomposing a number leading to a ten (e.g., $13 - 4 = 13 - 3 - 1 = 10 - 1 = 9$); using the relationship between addition and subtraction (e.g., knowing that $8 + 4 = 12$, one knows $12 - 8 = 4$); and creating equivalent but easier known sums (e.g., adding $6 + 7$ by creating the known equivalent $6 + 6 + 1 = 12 + 1 = 13$).	1 day
Unit 2 ADDITION AND SUBTRACTION SITUATIONS AND DATA		
Module 5: Understand Add To and Take From Problems		
Lesson 5.1 Represent Result Unknown Problems with Objects and Drawings	Use addition and subtraction within 20 to solve word problems involving situations of adding to, taking from, putting together, taking apart, and comparing, with unknowns in all positions, e.g., by using objects, drawings, and equations with a symbol for the unknown number to represent the problem.	1 day
Lesson 5.2 Represent Change Unknown Problems with Objects and Drawings	Use addition and subtraction within 20 to solve word problems involving situations of adding to, taking from, putting together, taking apart, and comparing, with unknowns in all positions, e.g., by using objects, drawings, and equations with a symbol for the unknown number to represent the problem.	1 day
Lesson 5.3 Represent Start Unknown Problems with Objects and Drawings	Use addition and subtraction within 20 to solve word problems involving situations of adding to, taking from, putting together, taking apart, and comparing, with unknowns in all positions, e.g., by using objects, drawings, and equations with a symbol for the unknown number to represent the problem.	1 day
Lesson 5.4 Solve Add To and Take From Problems	Use addition and subtraction within 20 to solve word problems involving situations of adding to, taking from, putting together, taking apart, and comparing, with unknowns in all positions, e.g., by using objects, drawings, and equations with a symbol for the unknown number to represent the problem.	2 days
Module 6: Understand Put Together and Take Apart Problems		
Lesson 6.1 Represent Total Unknown Problems with Objects and Drawings	Use addition and subtraction within 20 to solve word problems involving situations of adding to, taking from, putting together, taking apart, and comparing, with unknowns in all positions, e.g., by using objects, drawings, and equations with a symbol for the unknown number to represent the problem.	1 day
Lesson 6.2 Represent Both Addends Unknown Problems with Objects and Drawings	Use addition and subtraction within 20 to solve word problems involving situations of adding to, taking from, putting together, taking apart, and comparing, with unknowns in all positions, e.g., by using objects, drawings, and equations with a symbol for the unknown number to represent the problem.	1 day

Lesson	Mathematics Standards, Grade 1	Pacing
Lesson 6.3 Represent Addend Unknown Problems with Objects and Drawings	■ Use addition and subtraction within 20 to solve word problems involving situations of adding to, taking from, putting together, taking apart, and comparing, with unknowns in all positions, e.g., by using objects, drawings, and equations with a symbol for the unknown number to represent the problem.	1 day
Lesson 6.4 Represent Total Unknown Problems with a Visual Model	■ Use addition and subtraction within 20 to solve word problems involving situations of adding to, taking from, putting together, taking apart, and comparing, with unknowns in all positions, e.g., by using objects, drawings, and equations with a symbol for the unknown number to represent the problem.	2 days
Lesson 6.5 Represent Addend Unknown and Both Addends Unknown Problems with a Visual Model	■ Use addition and subtraction within 20 to solve word problems involving situations of adding to, taking from, putting together, taking apart, and comparing, with unknowns in all positions, e.g., by using objects, drawings, and equations with a symbol for the unknown number to represent the problem.	2 days
Lesson 6.6 Solve Put Together and Take Apart Problems	■ Use addition and subtraction within 20 to solve word problems involving situations of adding to, taking from, putting together, taking apart, and comparing, with unknowns in all position, e.g., by using objects, drawings, and equations with a symbol for the unknown number to represent the problem.	1 day
Lesson 6.7 Solve Addition and Subtraction Problems	■ Use addition and subtraction within 20 to solve word problems involving situations of adding to, taking from, putting together, taking apart, and comparing, with unknowns in all positions, e.g., by using objects, drawings, and equations with a symbol for the unknown number to represent the problem.	2 days
Module 7: Understand Compare Problems		
Lesson 7.1 Represent Difference Unknown Problems with Objects and Drawings	■ Use addition and subtraction within 20 to solve word problems involving situations of adding to, taking from, putting together, taking apart, and comparing, with unknowns in all positions, e.g., by using objects, drawings, and equations with a symbol for the unknown number to represent the problem.	1 day
Lesson 7.2 Represent Bigger Unknown Problems with Objects and Drawings	■ Use addition and subtraction within 20 to solve word problems involving situations of adding to, taking from, putting together, taking apart, and comparing, with unknowns in all positions, e.g., by using objects, drawings, and equations with a symbol for the unknown number to represent the problem.	1 day
Lesson 7.3 Represent Smaller Unknown Problems with Objects and Drawings	■ Use addition and subtraction within 20 to solve word problems involving situations of adding to, taking from, putting together, taking apart, and comparing, with unknowns in all positions, e.g., by using objects, drawings, and equations with a symbol for the unknown number to represent the problem.	1 day

Module continued on next page →

Pacing Guide

Lesson		Mathematics Standards, Grade 1	Pacing
Module 7: **Understand Compare Problems**			
Lesson 7.4 Represent Difference Unknown Problems with a Visual Model	▪	Use addition and subtraction within 20 to solve word problems involving situations of adding to, taking from, putting together, taking apart, and comparing, with unknowns in all positions, e.g., by using objects, drawings, and equations with a symbol for the unknown number to represent the problem.	2 days
Lesson 7.5 Represent Bigger Unknown and Smaller Unknown Problems with a Visual Model	▪	Use addition and subtraction within 20 to solve word problems involving situations of adding to, taking from, putting together, taking apart, and comparing, with unknowns in all positions, e.g., by using objects, drawings, and equations with a symbol for the unknown number to represent the problem.	2 days
Lesson 7.6 Use Strategies to Solve Compare Problems	▪	Use addition and subtraction within 20 to solve word problems involving situations of adding to, taking from, putting together, taking apart, and comparing, with unknowns in all positions, e.g., by using objects, drawings, and equations with a symbol for the unknown number to represent the problem.	1 day
Lesson 7.7 Solve Addition and Subtraction Situations	▪	Use addition and subtraction within 20 to solve word problems involving situations of adding to, taking from, putting together, taking apart, and comparing, with unknowns in all positions, e.g., by using objects, drawings, and equations with a symbol for the unknown number to represent the problem.	2 days
Module 8: **Data**			
Lesson 8.1 Interpret Picture Graphs	☐	Organize, represent, and interpret data with up to three categories; ask and answer questions about the total number of data points, how many in each category, and how many more or less are in one category than in another.	1 day
Lesson 8.2 Represent Data with Picture Graphs	☐	Organize, represent, and interpret data with up to three categories; ask and answer questions about the total number of data points, how many in each category, and how many more or less are in one category than in another.	1 day
Lesson 8.3 Interpret Tally Charts	☐	Organize, represent, and interpret data with up to three categories; ask and answer questions about the total number of data points, how many in each category, and how many more or less are in one category than in another.	1 day
Lesson 8.4 Represent Data with Tally Charts	☐	Organize, represent, and interpret data with up to three categories; ask and answer questions about the total number of data points, how many in each category, and how many more or less are in one category than in another.	1 day
Lesson 8.5 Interpret Bar Graphs	☐	Organize, represent, and interpret data with up to three categories; ask and answer questions about the total number of data points, how many in each category, and how many more or less are in one category than in another.	1 day
Lesson 8.6 Represent Data with Bar Graphs	☐	Organize, represent, and interpret data with up to three categories; ask and answer questions about the total number of data points, how many in each category, and how many more or less are in one category than in another.	1 day

Lesson		Mathematics Standards, Grade 1	Pacing
○ Lesson 8.7 Use Data to Solve Problems	□	Organize, represent, and interpret data with up to three categories; ask and answer questions about the total number of data points, how many in each category, and how many more or less are in one category than in another.	1 day

Unit 3   NUMBERS TO 120

Module 9:   Understand Place Value

○ Lesson 9.1 Make Ten and Ones	■	10 can be thought of as a bundle of ten ones—called a "ten."	1 day
	■	The numbers from 11 to 19 are composed of a ten and one, two, three, four, five, six, seven, eight, or nine ones.	
○ Lesson 9.2 Understand Ten and Ones	■	10 can be thought of as a bundle of ten ones—called a "ten."	1 day
	■	The numbers from 11 to 19 are composed of a ten and one, two, three, four, five, six, seven, eight, or nine ones.	
○ Lesson 9.3 Make Tens	■	10 can be thought of as a bundle of ten ones—called a "ten."	1 day
	■	The numbers 10, 20, 30, 40, 50, 60, 70, 80, 90 refer to one, two, three, four, five, six, seven, eight, or nine tens (and 0 ones).	

Module 10:   Count and Represent Numbers

○ Lesson 10.1 Count to 120	■	Count to 120, starting at any number less than 120. In this range, read and write numerals and represent a number of objects with a written numeral.	1 day
○ Lesson 10.2 Represent Numbers as Tens and Ones with Objects	■	Understand that the two digits of a two-digit number represent amounts of tens and ones.	1 day
○ Lesson 10.3 Represent Numbers as Tens and Ones with Drawings	■	Understand that the two digits of a two-digit number represent amounts of tens and ones.	1 day
○ Lesson 10.4 Decompose Numbers in Different Ways	■	10 can be thought of as a bundle of ten ones—called a "ten."	2 days
○ Lesson 10.5 Represent, Read, and Write Numbers from 100 to 110	■	Count to 120, starting at any number less than 120. In this range, read and write numerals and represent a number of objects with a written numeral.	1 day
○ Lesson 10.6 Represent, Read, and Write Numbers from 110 to 120	■	Count to 120, starting at any number less than 120. In this range, read and write numerals and represent a number of objects with a written numeral.	1 day

Pacing Guide

Lesson	Mathematics Standards, Grade 1	Pacing
Module 11: **Compare Numbers**		
Lesson 11.1 Understand Greater Than	■ Compare two two-digit numbers based on meanings of the tens and ones digits, recording the results of comparisons with the symbols >, =, and <.	1 day
Lesson 11.2 Understand Less Than	■ Compare two two-digit numbers based on meanings of the tens and ones digits, recording the results of comparisons with the symbols >, =, and <.	1 day
Lesson 11.3 Use Symbols to Compare	■ Compare two two-digit numbers based on meanings of the tens and ones digits, recording the results of comparisons with the symbols >, =, and <. ■ Understand the meaning of the equal sign, and determine if equations involving addition and subtraction are true or false.	1 day
Lesson 11.4 Compare Numbers	■ Compare two two-digit numbers based on meanings of the tens and ones digits, recording the results of comparisons with the symbols >, =, and <.	2 days

Lesson	Mathematics Standards, Grade 1	Pacing
Unit 4　ADDITION AND SUBTRACTION IN BASE TEN		
Module 12:　Understand Addition and Subtraction with Tens and Ones		
○ Lesson 12.1　Represent Adding Tens	■ Add within 100, including adding a two-digit number and a one-digit number, and adding a two-digit number and a multiple of 10, using concrete models or drawings and strategies based on place value, properties of operations, and/or the relationship between addition and subtraction; relate the strategy to a written method and explain the reasoning used. Understand that in adding two-digit numbers, one adds tens and tens, ones and ones; and sometimes it is necessary to compose a ten.	1 day
○ Lesson 12.2　Represent Subtracting Tens	■ Subtract multiples of 10 in the range 10–90 from multiples of 10 in the range 10–90 (positive or zero differences), using concrete models or drawings and strategies based on place value, properties of operations, and/or the relationship between addition and subtraction; relate the strategy to a written method and explain the reasoning used.	1 day
○ Lesson 12.3　Add or Subtract Tens	■ Add within 100, including adding a two-digit number and a one-digit number, and adding a two-digit number and a multiple of 10, using concrete models or drawings and strategies based on place value, properties of operations, and/or the relationship between addition and subtraction; relate the strategy to a written method and explain the reasoning used. Understand that in adding two-digit numbers, one adds tens and tens, ones and ones; and sometimes it is necessary to compose a ten. ■ Subtract multiples of 10 in the range 10–90 from multiples of 10 in the range 10–90 (positive or zero differences), using concrete models or drawings and strategies based on place value, properties of operations, and/or the relationship between addition and subtraction; relate the strategy to a written method and explain the reasoning used.	1 day
○ Lesson 12.4　Use a Hundred Chart to Add	■ Add within 100, including adding a two-digit number and a one-digit number, and adding a two-digit number and a multiple of 10, using concrete models or drawings and strategies based on place value, properties of operations, and/or the relationship between addition and subtraction; relate the strategy to a written method and explain the reasoning used. Understand that in adding two-digit numbers, one adds tens and tens, ones and ones; and sometimes it is necessary to compose a ten.	1 day
○ Lesson 12.5　Represent Addition with Tens and Ones	■ Add within 100, including adding a two-digit number and a one-digit number, and adding a two-digit number and a multiple of 10, using concrete models or drawings and strategies based on place value, properties of operations, and/or the relationship between addition and subtraction; relate the strategy to a written method and explain the reasoning used. Understand that in adding two-digit numbers, one adds tens and tens, ones and ones; and sometimes it is necessary to compose a ten.	1 day

Module continued on next page →

Pacing Guide

Lesson	Mathematics Standards, Grade 1	Pacing
Module 12: **Understand Addition and Subtraction with Tens and Ones**		
Lesson 12.6 Represent Make Ten to Add	■ Add within 100, including adding a two-digit number and a one-digit number, and adding a two-digit number and a multiple of 10, using concrete models or drawings and strategies based on place value, properties of operations, and/or the relationship between addition and subtraction; relate the strategy to a written method and explain the reasoning used. Understand that in adding two-digit numbers, one adds tens and tens, ones and ones; and sometimes it is necessary to compose a ten.	2 days
Lesson 12.7 Represent Make Ten to Add with a Visual Model	■ Add within 100, including adding a two-digit number and a one-digit number, and adding a two-digit number and a multiple of 10, using concrete models or drawings and strategies based on place value, properties of operations, and/or the relationship between addition and subtraction; relate the strategy to a written method and explain the reasoning used. Understand that in adding two-digit numbers, one adds tens and tens, ones and ones; and sometimes it is necessary to compose a ten.	1 day
Lesson 12.8 Use Mental Math to Find 10 Less and 10 More	■ Given a two-digit number, mentally find 10 more or 10 less than the number, without having to count; explain the reasoning used.	1 day
Module 13 **Two-Digit Addition and Subtraction**		
Lesson 13.1 Use a Hundred Chart to Show Two-Digit Addition and Subtraction	■ Add within 100, including adding a two-digit number and a one-digit number, and adding a two-digit number and a multiple of 10, using concrete models or drawings and strategies based on place value, properties of operations, and/or the relationship between addition and subtraction; relate the strategy to a written method and explain the reasoning used. Understand that in adding two-digit numbers, one adds tens and tens, ones and ones; and sometimes it is necessary to compose a ten. ■ Subtract multiples of 10 in the range 10–90 from multiples of 10 in the range 10–90 (positive or zero differences), using concrete models or drawings and strategies based on place value, properties of operations, and/or the relationship between addition and subtraction; relate the strategy to a written method and explain the reasoning used.	1 day
Lesson 13.2 Understand and Explain Place Value Addition	■ Add within 100, including adding a two-digit number and a one-digit number, and adding a two-digit number and a multiple of 10, using concrete models or drawings and strategies based on place value, properties of operations, and/or the relationship between addition and subtraction; relate the strategy to a written method and explain the reasoning used. Understand that in adding two-digit numbers, one adds tens and tens, ones and ones; and sometimes it is necessary to compose a ten.	1 day

Lesson	Mathematics Standards, Grade 1	Pacing
Lesson 13.3 Understand and Explain Place Value Subtraction	■ Subtract multiples of 10 in the range 10–90 from multiples of 10 in the range 10–90 (positive or zero differences), using concrete models or drawings and strategies based on place value, properties of operations, and/or the relationship between addition and subtraction; relate the strategy to a written method and explain the reasoning used.	1 day
Lesson 13.4 Solve Two-Digit Addition and Subtraction Problems	■ Add within 100, including adding a two-digit number and a one-digit number, and adding a two-digit number and a multiple of 10, using concrete models or drawings and strategies based on place value, properties of operations, and/or the relationship between addition and subtraction; relate the strategy to a written method and explain the reasoning used. Understand that in adding two-digit numbers, one adds tens and tens, ones and ones; and sometimes it is necessary to compose a ten. ■ Subtract multiples of 10 in the range 10–90 from multiples of 10 in the range 10–90 (positive or zero differences), using concrete models or drawings and strategies based on place value, properties of operations, and/or the relationship between addition and subtraction; relate the strategy to a written method and explain the reasoning used.	1 day
Lesson 13.5 Practice Facts to 20	■ Add and subtract within 20, demonstrating fluency for addition and subtraction within 10. Use strategies such as counting on; making ten (e.g., $8 + 6 = 8 + 2 + 4 = 10 + 4 + 14$); decomposing a number leading to a ten (e.g., $13 - 4 = 13 - 3 - 1 = 10 - 1 = 9$); using the relationship between addition and subtraction (e.g., knowing that $8 + 4 = 12$, one knows $12 - 8 = 4$); and creating equivalent but easier or known sums (e.g., adding $6 + 7$ by creating the known equivalent $6 + 6 + 1 = 12 + 1 = 13$).	1 day
Lesson 13.6 Practice Two-Digit Addition and Subtraction	■ Add within 100, including adding a two-digit number and a one-digit number, and adding a two-digit number and a multiple of 10, using concrete models or drawings and strategies based on place value, properties of operations, and/or the relationship between addition and subtraction; relate the strategy to a written method and explain the reasoning used. Understand that in adding two-digit numbers, one adds tens and tens, ones and ones; and sometimes it is necessary to compose a ten. ■ Subtract multiples of 10 in the range 10–90 from multiples of 10 in the range 10–90 (positive or zero differences), using concrete models or drawings and strategies based on place value, properties of operations, and/or the relationship between addition and subtraction; relate the strategy to a written method and explain the reasoning used.	1 day

Pacing Guide

Lesson	Mathematics Standards, Grade 1	Pacing
Unit 5 GEOMETRY		
Module 14: Three-Dimensional Shapes		
Lesson 14.1 Describe and Draw Three-Dimensional Shapes	Distinguish between defining attributes (e.g., triangles are closed and three-sided) versus non-defining attributes (e.g., color, orientation, overall size); build and draw shapes to possess defining attributes.	2 days
Lesson 14.2 Compose Three-Dimensional Shapes	Compose two-dimensional shapes (rectangles, squares, trapezoids, triangles, half-circles, and quarter-circles) or three-dimensional shapes (cubes, right rectangular prisms, right circular cones, and right circular cylinders) to create a composite shape, and compose new shapes from the composite shape.	1 day
Lesson 14.3 Make New Three-Dimensional Shapes	Compose two-dimensional shapes (rectangles, squares, trapezoids, triangles, half-circles, and quarter-circles) or three-dimensional shapes (cubes, right rectangular prisms, right circular cones, and right circular cylinders) to create a composite shape, and compose new shapes from the composite shape.	1 day
Module 15: Two-Dimensional Shapes		
Lesson 15.1 Sort Two-Dimensional Shapes by Attribute	Distinguish between defining attributes (e.g., triangles are closed and three-sided) versus non-defining attributes (e.g., color, orientation, overall size); build and draw shapes to possess defining attributes.	1 day
Lesson 15.2 Describe and Draw Two-Dimensional Shapes	Distinguish between defining attributes (e.g., triangles are closed and three-sided) versus non-defining attributes (e.g., color, orientation, overall size); build and draw shapes to possess defining attributes.	1 day
Lesson 15.3 Compose Two-Dimensional Shapes	Compose two-dimensional shapes (rectangles, squares, trapezoids, triangles, half-circles, and quarter-circles) or three-dimensional shapes (cubes, right rectangular prisms, right circular cones, and right circular cylinders) to create a composite shape, and compose new shapes from the composite shape.	1 day
Lesson 15.4 Identify Composed Shapes	Compose two-dimensional shapes (rectangles, squares, trapezoids, triangles, half-circles, and quarter-circles) or three-dimensional shapes (cubes, right rectangular prisms, right circular cones, and right circular cylinders) to create a composite shape, and compose new shapes from the composite shape.	1 day
Lesson 15.5 Make New Two-Dimensional Shapes	Compose two-dimensional shapes (rectangles, squares, trapezoids, triangles, half-circles, and quarter-circles) or three-dimensional shapes (cubes, right rectangular prisms, right circular cones, and right circular cylinders) to create a composite shape, and compose new shapes from the composite shape.	1 day

Lesson	Mathematics Standards, Grade 1	Pacing
Module 16:　Fraction Foundations		
◯ Lesson 16.1　Take Apart Two-Dimensional Shapes	◯ Partition circles and rectangles into two and four equal shares, describe the shares using the words *halves, fourths,* and *quarters,* and use the phrases *half of, fourth of,* and *quarter of.* Describe the whole as two of, or four of the shares. Understand for these examples that decomposing into more equal shares creates smaller shares.	1 day
◯ Lesson 16.2　Identify Equal or Unequal Shares	◯ Partition circles and rectangles into two and four equal shares, describe the shares using the words *halves, fourths,* and *quarters,* and use the phrases *half of, fourth of,* and *quarter of.* Describe the whole as two of, or four of the shares. Understand for these examples that decomposing into more equal shares creates smaller shares.	1 day
◯ Lesson 16.3　Partition Shapes into Halves	◯ Partition circles and rectangles into two and four equal shares, describe the shares using the words *halves, fourths,* and *quarters,* and use the phrases *half of, fourth of,* and *quarter of.* Describe the whole as two of, or four of the shares. Understand for these examples that decomposing into more equal shares creates smaller shares.	1 day
◯ Lesson 16.4　Partition Shapes into Fourths	◯ Partition circles and rectangles into two and four equal shares, describe the shares using the words *halves, fourths,* and *quarters,* and use the phrases *half of, fourth of,* and *quarter of.* Describe the whole as two of, or four of the shares. Understand for these examples that decomposing into more equal shares creates smaller shares.	1 day

Pacing Guide

Lesson		Mathematics Standards, Grade 1	Pacing
Unit 6 MEASUREMENT			
Module 17: Measure Length			
Lesson 17.1	Order Length	Order three objects by length; compare the lengths of two objects indirectly by using a third object.	1 day
Lesson 17.2	Use Indirect Measurement to Compare Length	Order three objects by length; compare the lengths of two objects indirectly by using a third object.	1 day
Lesson 17.3	Use Nonstandard Units to Measure Length	Express the length of an object as a whole number of length units, by laying multiple copies of a shorter object (the length unit) end to end; understand that the length measurement of an object is the number of same-size length units that span it with no gaps or overlaps.	1 day
Lesson 17.4	Make a Nonstandard Measuring Tool	Express the length of an object as a whole number of length units, by laying multiple copies of a shorter object (the length unit) end to end; understand that the length measurement of an object is the number of same-size length units that span it with no gaps or overlaps.	1 day
Module 18: Measure Time			
Lesson 18.1	Understand Time to the Hour	Tell and write time in hours and half-hours using analog and digital clocks.	1 day
Lesson 18.2	Understand Time to the Half Hour	Tell and write time in hours and half-hours using analog and digital clocks.	1 day
Lesson 18.3	Tell Time to the Hour and Half Hour	Tell and write time in hours and half-hours using analog and digital clocks.	1 day
Lesson 18.4	Practice Time to the Hour and Half Hour	Tell and write time in hours and half-hours using analog and digital clocks.	1 day

End-of-Year Options

Getting Ready Lessons

A variety of end-of-year options are available for teachers who aim to complete core instruction before a high-stakes assessment is administered. Utilizing standards reports or the recommendations tool, you can find and review content that students did not master or retain. Or, you can use the Getting Ready lessons. These lessons present on-grade-level content that is essential for setting a foundation for success with next year's content.

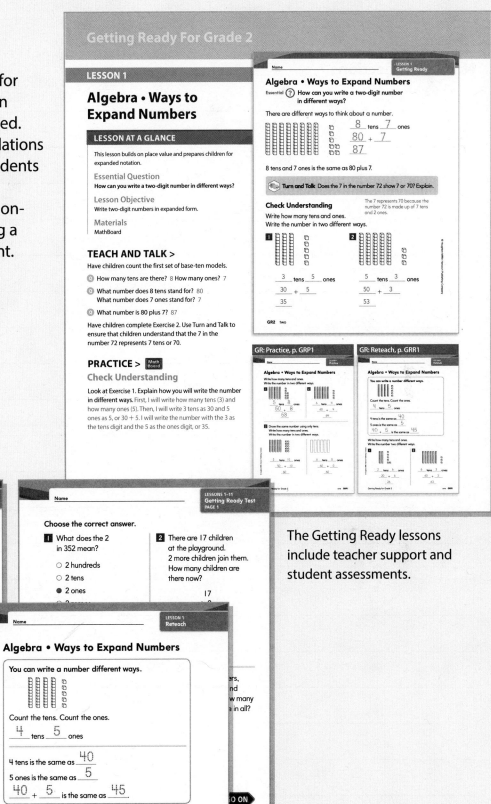

The Getting Ready lessons include teacher support and student assessments.

Teacher Notes

Notes & Reflections

Correlations

ONLINE

Search by state standard for standard-specific resources on Ed, Your Friend in Learning.

Standards and Mathematical Practices and Processes

Standards	Student Edition Lessons
Domain OPERATIONS AND ALGEBRAIC THINKING	
Cluster: Represent and solve problems involving addition and subtraction.	
Use addition and subtraction within 20 to solve word problems involving situations of adding to, taking from, putting together, taking apart, and comparing, with unknowns in all positions, e.g., by using objects, drawings, and equations with a symbol for the unknown number to represent the problem.	1.1, 1.7, 2.1, 2.6, 4.6, 5.1, 5.2, 5.3, 5.4, 6.1, 6.2, 6.3, 6.4, 6.5, 6.6, 6.7, 7.1, 7.2, 7.3, 7.4, 7.5, 7.6, 7.7
Solve word problems that call for addition of three whole numbers whose sum is less than or equal to 20, e.g., by using objects, drawings, and equations with a symbol for the unknown number to represent the problem.	3.3, 3.4, 3.5
Cluster: Understand and apply properties of operations and the relationship between addition and subtraction.	
Apply properties of operations as strategies to add and subtract.	3.1, 3.2, 3.3, 3.4, 3.5
Understand subtraction as an unknown-addend problem.	2.4, 4.1
Cluster: Add and subtract within 20.	
Relate counting to addition and subtraction (e.g., by counting on 2 to add 2).	1.2, 2.2, 2.3
Add and subtract within 20, demonstrating fluency for addition and subtraction within 10. Use strategies such as counting on; making ten (e.g., $8 + 6 = 8 + 2 + 4 = 10 + 4 = 14$); decomposing a number leading to a ten (e.g., $13 - 4 = 13 - 3 - 1 = 10 - 1 = 9$); using the relationship between addition and subtraction (e.g., knowing that $8 + 4 = 12$, one knows $12 - 8 = 4$); and creating equivalent but easier or known sums (e.g., adding $6 + 7$ by creating the known equivalent $6 + 6 + 1 = 12 + 1 = 13$).	1.3, 1.4, 1.5, 1.6, 1.7, 2.4, 2.5, 2.6, 3.7, 4.1, 4.2, 4.3, 4.4, 4.7, 13.5
Cluster: Work with addition and subtraction equations.	
Understand the meaning of the equal sign, and determine if equations involving addition and subtraction are true or false.	3.6, 11.3
Determine the unknown whole number in an addition or subtraction equation relating to three whole numbers.	2.4, 4.1, 4.5, 4.6

Correlations

Standards	Student Edition Lessons
Domain NUMBER AND OPERATIONS IN BASE TEN	
Cluster: Extend the counting sequence.	
Count to 120, starting at any number less than 120. In this range, read and write numerals and represent a number of objects with a written numeral.	10.1, 10.5, 10.6
Cluster: Understand place value.	
Understand that the two digits of a two-digit number represent amounts of tens and ones.	10.2, 10.3
• 10 can be thought of as a bundle of ten ones—called a "ten."	9.1, 9.2, 9.3, 10.4
• The numbers from 11 to 19 are composed of a ten and one, two, three, four, five, six, seven, eight, or nine ones.	9.1, 9.2
• The numbers 10, 20, 30, 40, 50, 60, 70, 80, 90 refer to one, two, three, four, five, six, seven, eight, or nine tens (and 0 ones).	9.3
Compare two two-digit numbers based on meanings of the tens and ones digits, recording the results of comparisons with the symbols >, =, and <.	11.1, 11.2, 11.3, 11.4
Cluster: Use place value understanding and properties of operations to add and subtract.	
Add within 100, including adding a two-digit number and a one-digit number, and adding a two-digit number and a multiple of 10, using concrete models or drawings and strategies based on place value, properties of operations, and/or the relationship between addition and subtraction; relate the strategy to a written method and explain the reasoning used. Understand that in adding two-digit numbers, one adds tens and tens, ones and ones; and sometimes it is necessary to compose a ten.	12.1, 12.3, 12.4, 12.5, 12.6, 12.7, 13.1, 13.2, 13.4, 13.6
Given a two-digit number, mentally find 10 more or 10 less than the number, without having to count; explain the reasoning used.	12.8
Subtract multiples of 10 in the range 10–90 from multiples of 10 in the range 10–90 (positive or zero differences), using concrete models or drawings and strategies based on place value, properties of operations, and/or the relationship between addition and subtraction; relate the strategy to a written method and explain the reasoning used.	12.2, 12.3, 13.1, 13.3, 13.4, 13.6
Domain MEASUREMENT AND DATA	
Cluster: Measure lengths indirectly and by iterating length units.	
Order three objects by length; compare the lengths of two objects indirectly by using a third object.	17.1, 17.2
Express the length of an object as a whole number of length units, by laying multiple copies of a shorter object (the length unit) end to end; understand that the length measurement of an object is the number of same-size length units that span it with no gaps or overlaps.	17.3, 17.4

Standards	Student Edition Lessons
Cluster: Tell and write time.	
Tell and write time in hours and half-hours using analog and digital clocks.	18.1, 18.2, 18.3, 18.4
Cluster: Represent and interpret data.	
Organize, represent, and interpret data with up to three categories; ask and answer questions about the total number of data points, how many in each category, and how many more or less are in one category than in another.	8.1, 8.2, 8.3, 8.4, 8.5, 8.6, 8.7
Domain GEOMETRY	
Cluster: Reason with shapes and their attributes.	
Distinguish between defining attributes (e.g., triangles are closed and three-sided) versus non-defining attributes (e.g., color, orientation, overall size); build and draw shapes to possess defining attributes.	14.1, 15.1, 15.2
Compose two-dimensional shapes (rectangles, squares, trapezoids, triangles, half-circles, and quarter-circles) or three-dimensional shapes (cubes, right rectangular prisms, right circular cones, and right circular cylinders) to create a composite shape and compose new shapes from the composite shape.	14.2, 14.3, 15.3, 15.4, 15.5
Partition circles and rectangles into two and four equal shares, describe the shares using the words *halves, fourths,* and *quarters*, and use the phrases *half of, fourth of*, and *quarter of*. Describe the whole as two of, or four of the shares. Understand for these examples that decomposing into more equal shares creates smaller shares.	16.1, 16.2, 16.3, 16.4

Correlations

Mathematical Practices and Processes	Student Edition Lessons
Into Math covers all Mathematical Practice and Process standards as an integral part of instruction and practice. For a summary of how the program features address each Mathematical Practice and Process standard see PG18-PG19. These pages include probing *Questions to Ask* that support each Mathematical Practice and Process standard.	
Make sense of problems and persevere in solving them. Mathematically proficient students start by explaining to themselves the meaning of a problem and looking for entry points to its solution. They analyze givens, constraints, relationships, and goals. They make conjectures about the form and meaning of the solution and plan a solution pathway rather than simply jumping into a solution attempt. They consider analogous problems, and try special cases and simpler forms of the original problem in order to gain insight into its solution. They monitor and evaluate their progress and change course if necessary. Other students might, depending on the context of the problem, transform algebraic expressions or change the viewing window on their graphing calculator to get the information they need. Mathematically proficient students can explain correspondences between equations, verbal descriptions, tables, and graphs or draw diagrams of important features and relationships, graph data, and search for regularity of trends. Younger students might rely on using concrete objects or pictures to help conceptualize and solve a problem. Mathematically proficient students check their answers to problems using a different method, and they continually ask themselves, "Does this make sense?" They can understand the approaches of others to solving complex problems and identify correspondences between different approaches.	In every lesson. Some examples include 1.2, 2.6, 3.5, 6.7, 10.3, 14.1, 15.3, 16.4, 17.4, 18.2
Reason abstractly and quantitatively. Mathematically proficient students make sense of quantities and their relationships in problem situations. They bring two complementary abilities to bear on problems involving quantitative relationships: the ability to *decontextualize*—to abstract a given situation and represent it symbolically and manipulate the representing symbols as if they have a life of their own, without necessarily attending to their referents—and the ability to *contextualize*, to pause as needed during the manipulation process in order to probe into the referents for the symbols involved. Quantitative reasoning entails habits of creating a coherent representation of the problem at hand; considering the units involved; attending to the meaning of quantities, not just how to compute them; and knowing and flexibly using different properties of operations and objects.	1.4, 1.6, 1.7, 2.1, 2.3, 2.5, 2.6, 3.3, 3.5, 3.6, 4.1, 5.1, 5.2, 5.4, 6.1, 6.2, 6.3, 6.4, 6.7, 7.4, 7.5, 8.1, 8.2, 8.3, 8.5, 8.6, 9.1, 9.2, 9.3, 10.1, 11.1, 11.2, 12.1, 12.3, 12.6, 12.7, 12.8, 13.1, 13.5, 13.6, 17.2, 18.4
Construct viable arguments and critique the reasoning of others. Mathematically proficient students understand and use stated assumptions, definitions, and previously established results in constructing arguments. They make conjectures and build a logical progression of statements to explore the truth of their conjectures. They are able to analyze situations by breaking them into cases, and can recognize and use counterexamples. They justify their conclusions, communicate them to others, and respond to arguments of others. They reason inductively about data, making plausible arguments that take into account the context from which the data arose. Mathematically proficient students are also able to compare the effectiveness of two plausible arguments, distinguish correct logic or reasoning from that which is flawed, and—if there is a flow in an argument—explain what is. Elementary students can construct arguments using concrete referents such as objects, drawings, diagrams, and actions. Such arguments can make sense and be correct, even though they are not domains to which an argument applies. Students at all grades can listen or read the arguments of others, decide whether they make sense, and ask useful questions to clarify or improve the arguments.	1.6, 1.7, 6.5, 7.6, 11.2, 12.4, 12.8, 13.4, 15.2, 16.2, 16.3, 17.1

Mathematical Practices and Processes	Student Edition Lessons
Model with mathematics. Mathematically proficient students can apply the mathematics they know to solve problems arising in everyday life, society, and the workplace. In early grades, this might be as simple as writing an addition equation to describe a situation. In middle grades, a student might apply proportional reasoning to plan a school event or analyze a problem in the community. By high school, a student might use geometry to solve a design problem or use a function to describe how one quantity of interest depends on another. Mathematically proficient students who can apply what they know are comfortable making assumptions and approximations to simplify a complicated situation, realizing that these may need revision later. They are able to identify important quantities in a practical situation and map their relationships using such tools as diagrams, two-way tables, graphs, flowcharts and formulas. They can analyze those relationships mathematically to draw conclusions. They routinely interpret their mathematical results in the context of the situation and reflect on whether the results make sense, possibly improving the model if it has not served its purpose.	1.1, 2.1, 2.4, 3.1, 3.2, 3.5, 3.7, 4.4, 4.5, 4.6, 4.7, 5.1, 5.2, 5.3, 5.4, 6.1, 6.2, 6.3, 6.4, 6.5, 6.6, 7.1, 7.2, 8.6, 12.1, 12.2, 12.4, 12.5, 12.7, 13.2, 13.3, 13.6
Use appropriate tools strategically. Mathematically proficient students consider the available tools when solving a mathematical problem. These tools might include pencil and paper, concrete models, a ruler, a protractor, a calculator, a spreadsheet, a computer algebra system, a statistical package, or dynamic geometry software. Proficient students are sufficiently familiar with tools appropriate for their grade or course to make sound decisions about when each of these tools might be helpful, recognizing both the insight to be gained and their limitations. For example, mathematically proficient high school students analyze graphs of functions and solutions generated using a graphing calculator. They detect possible errors by strategically using estimation and other mathematical knowledge. When making mathematical models, they know that technology can enable them to visualize the results of varying assumptions, explore consequences, and compare predictions with data. Mathematically proficient students at various grade levels are able to identify relevant external mathematical resources, such as digital content located on a website and use them to pose or solve problems. They are able to use technological tools to explore and deepen their understanding of concepts.	In every Spark Your Learning, Module Review, and the following lessons: 1.1, 1.2, 1.3, 1.4, 2.2, 2.3, 2.5, 2.6, 4.1, 4.2, 4.3, 5.3, 7.2, 7.3, 7.4, 7.5, 8.4, 8.7, 10.2, 10.3, 10.4, 10.5, 10.6, 12.4, 12.6, 13.1, 14.1, 14.3, 15.3, 15.4, 16.4, 17.3, 17.4, 18.1, 18.3, 18.4
Attend to precision. Mathematically proficient students try to communicate precisely to others. They try to use clear definitions in discussion with others and in their own reasoning. They state the meaning of the symbols they choose, including using the equal sign consistently and appropriately. They are careful about specifying units of measure, and labeling axes to clarify the correspondence with quantities in a problem. They calculate accurately and efficiently, express numerical answers with a degree of precision appropriate for the problem context. In the elementary grades, students give carefully formulated explanations to each other. By the time they reach high school they have learned to examine claims and make explicit use of definitions.	3.6, 3.7, 6.7, 8.1, 8.2, 8.3, 8.4, 8.5, 8.7, 10.2, 10.3, 11.2, 11.3, 11.4, 12.5, 13.4, 13.5, 14.2, 15.3, 15.4, 15.5, 16.1, 16.2, 16.3, 17.1, 17.3, 17.4, 18.2, 18.3

Correlations

Mathematical Practices and Processes	Student Edition Lessons
Look for and make use of structure. Mathematically proficient students look closely to discern a pattern or structure. Young students, for example, might notice that three and seven more is the same amount as seven and three more, or they may sort a collection of shapes according to how many sides the shapes have. Later, students will see 7×8 equals the well remembered $7 \times 5 + 7 \times 3$, in preparation for learning about the distributive property. In the expression $x^2 + 9x + 14$, older students can see the 14 as 2×7 and the 9 as $2 + 7$. They recognize the significance of an existing line in a geometric figure and can use the strategy of drawing an auxiliary line for solving problems. They also can step back for an overview and shift perspective. They can see complicated things, such as some algebraic expressions, as single objects or as being composed of several objects. For example, they can see $5 - 3(x - y)^2$ as 5 minus a positive number times a square and use that to realize that its value cannot be more than 5 for any real numbers x and y.	1.3, 1.4, 1.5, 2.4, 2.5, 3.1, 3.3, 3.4, 4.3, 4.4, 4.5, 4.7, 7.1, 7.3, 7.7, 9.1, 9.2, 9.3, 10.5, 10.6, 11.1, 11.3, 11.4, 12.1, 12.2, 13.2, 13.3, 14.2, 15.1, 15.2, 16.1, 16.2, 16.3, 16.4, 17.2, 18.1
Look for and express regularity in repeated reasoning. Mathematically proficient students notice if calculations are repeated, and look both for general methods and for shortcuts. Upper elementary students might notice when dividing 25 by 11 that they are repeating the same calculations over and over again, and conclude they have a repeating decimal. By paying attention to the calculation of slope as they repeatedly check whether points are on the line through (1, 2) with slope 3, middle school students might abstract the equation $(y - 2)/(x - 1) = 3$. Noticing the regularity in the way terms cancel when expanding $(x - 1)(x + 1)$, $(x - 1)(x^2 + x + 1)$, and $(x - 1)(x^3 + x^2 + x + 1)$ might lead them to the general formula for the sum of a geometric series. As they work to solve a problem, mathematically proficient students maintain oversight of the process, while attending to the details. They continually evaluate the reasonableness of their intermediate results.	1.5, 1.6, 2.2, 3.2, 3.4, 6.6, 7.3, 7.6, 7.7, 10.1, 10.4, 12.3, 14.2, 15.1, 15.5, 18.2

Jennifer Lempp
Educational Consultant
Alexandria, Virginia

Problem Solving Structures

Introducing Students to a Variety of Structures

We all want the same for students, to be independent problem solvers and thinkers. The types of problems we provide and the way we present them can ultimately support or hinder students. Most students are not given the opportunity to truly reason with a variety of word problems. Rather, students are often given problems that closely resemble the first problem below. The problem contains two numbers that you act upon in some way. The answer to the problem is unknown. However, students should be exposed to problems that have the start or the change unknown as well.

Let's consider these two problems:

- Anna has 7 books checked out from the library. She returns 4 books. How many books does Anna still have to return?

- Anna reads 7 books, and Jon reads 4 books. How many more books does Anna read than Jon?

Both problems could be solved using the equation $7 - 4 =$ _____. However, as students begin to translate story problems, the context of these problems varies quite a bit. The first can be considered a "take away" problem and the second a "compare" problem. If we always refer to subtraction as "take away," then we are removing the true context of the mathematics that exists in the world around us.

Various problem structures exist for addition, subtraction, multiplication, and division. Students do not need to be able to identify these structures, but it's important that teachers know the variety of structures and expose students to them.

Don't Steal the Struggle

The context within word problems helps to support mathematical thinking. Many teachers may shy away from problem solving, seeing it as more complex than a "numbers only" problem. However, students do not need to master the skill of computation in order to solve problems. In fact, the context used in problem solving can often help students make sense of the numbers, making the students more successful.

When introducing a word problem, don't be tempted to model a similar problem first and then give students a problem that simply contains different numbers. This results in stealing the students' struggle and takes away the opportunity for thinking and reasoning. Moreover, students should be encouraged to solve problems using whatever strategy or technique that they wish. It is also important to note that teachers should not teach "key words" to students as a system of support for students. Students are often told that words like "altogether" and "in all" are supposed to signal to students that they are to add, while words like "how many more" mean they are to subtract. However, key words can lead students to choose the wrong operation. Teaching key words takes away the thinking and sends the message that there is no reasoning necessary – that math is just about numbers and is not even a part of our real life. What is most important is their reasoning and why they chose to solve it in the way they did. The strategies used by students provide teachers with a great deal of information about where a student is and where to go next with him or her.

Problem Types

Addition and Subtraction Problem Situations–Add To/Take From

Add To/Take From problems have three components. There is an initial quantity–the **start**. The **change** is the action upon that initial quantity. The outcome of the action upon the initial quantity is the **result**.

	RESULT UNKNOWN	INTO MATH EXAMPLES
ADD TO	A problem in which the **start** and **change** (what is *added* to the start) are given in the problem. The **result** (the outcome of performing the action) is not known and is what the students determine.	There are 6 cats. 9 more join them. How many cats are there now? $6 + 9 = \blacksquare$ Example from Lesson 1.1, Task 2 • Additional Lessons 3.7, 5.1, 12.3, 12.5, 12.6, 12.7, 13.2
TAKE FROM	A problem in which the **start** and **change** (what is *taken from* the start) are given in the problem. The **result** (the outcome of performing the action) is not known and is what the students determine.	There are 8 balloons. 2 balloons float away. How many balloons are there now? $8 - 2 = \blacksquare$ Example from Lesson 2.1, Problem 1 • Additional Lessons 2.2, 2.5, 4.7, 5.1, 12.2, 13.3

	CHANGE UNKNOWN	INTO MATH EXAMPLES
ADD TO	A problem in which the **start** and **result** (the outcome of performing the action) are given in the problem. The **change** (what is added to the start) is not known and is what the students determine.	Calvin has 5 books. He gets more books. Now he has 15 books. How many books does he get? $5 + \blacksquare = 15$ Example from Lesson 5.4, Problem 10 • Additional Lessons 5.2, 13.1
TAKE FROM	A problem in which the **start** and **result** (the outcome of performing the action) are given in the problem. The **change** (what is taken from the start) is not known and is what the students determine.	Bea has 14 toy cars. She gives some to Jaylen. Now she has 8 toy cars. How many toy cars does Bea give to Jaylen? $14 - \blacksquare = 8$ Example from Lesson 5.2, Task 1 • Additional Lessons 5.4, 6.7, 7.7, 13.1, 13.6

	START UNKNOWN	INTO MATH EXAMPLES
ADD TO	A problem in which the **change** (what is *added to* the start) and **result** (the outcome of performing the action) are given in the problem. The **start** is not known and is what the students determine.	Sara has some stickers. She gets 9 stickers from a friend. Now she has 15 stickers. How many stickers did she have to start? $\blacksquare + 9 = 15$ Example from Lesson 5.3, Problem 2 · Additional Lessons 5.4, 7.7, 12.4
TAKE FROM	A problem in which the **change** (what is *taken from* the start) and **result** (the outcome of performing the action) are given in the problem. The **start** is not known and is what the students determine.	Max has some plants. He gives 4 plants to Bryce. Now he has 9 plants. How many plants did he have to start? $\blacksquare - 4 = 9$ Example from Lesson 5.3, Problem 3 · Additional Lessons 5.4, 6.7, 7.7

Problem Types

Addition and Subtraction Problem Situations—Put Together/Take Apart

In a *Put Together/Take Apart* problem, both quantities are already present. Unlike an *Add To/Take From* problem, these problems do not involve a change in the situation. The **total** is unknown or one or both of the **quantities** (or **groups**) are unknown.

	TOTAL UNKNOWN	INTO MATH EXAMPLES
PUT TOGETHER/ TAKE APART	A problem in which the **two groups/quantities** are known. The **total** is not known and is what the students determine.	There are 7 blue fish and 5 yellow fish in a tank. How many fish are in the tank? $7 + 5 = \blacksquare$ Example from Lesson 1.1, Task 1 · Additional Lessons 1.3, 1.5, 1.7, 3.1, 6.1, 6.4, 12.1, 13.2, 13.4
	ADDEND UNKNOWN	INTO MATH EXAMPLES
	A problem in which **one of the two groups/quantities** is known and the **total** is also known. The **other group/quantity** is not known and is what the students determine.	Trina writes 10 postcards. 6 are in the mail. The rest are on her desk. How many postcards are on her desk? $6 + \blacksquare = 10, 10 - 6 = \blacksquare$ Example from Lesson 2.4, Task 2 · Additional Lessons 2.5, 4.1, 4.2, 4.4, 6.3, 6.5, 6.6, 6.7, 7.7, 8.7
	BOTH ADDENDS UNKNOWN	INTO MATH EXAMPLES
	A problem in which the **total** is known. The **two groups/ quantities** are not known and are what the students determine.	Raul and Jon have 14 books altogether. How many books could each boy have? $10 = \blacksquare + \blacktriangle$ Example from Lesson 5.2, Task 1 · Additional Lessons 6.2, 6.5, 6.6, 6.7, 7.7, 13.5

Addition and Subtraction Problem Situations—Compare

Compare problems involve two separate quantities. In these problems, students seek to determine the larger quantity, the smaller quantity, or the difference between the two quantities.

COMPARE	DIFFERENCE UNKNOWN	INTO MATH EXAMPLES
	Version 1 Two known quantities are compared to find how many more there are of the **larger quantity**.	Daren has 3 cards. Marcia has 9 cards. How many more cards does Marcia have than Daren? $3 + \blacksquare = 9, 9 - 3 = \blacksquare$ Example from Lesson 7.1, Problem 3 • Additional Lessons 7.4, 7.6, 7.7, 13.3, 13.5
	Version 2 Two known quantities are compared to find how many fewer there are of the **smaller quantity**.	Ronald has 3 toys. Marcel has 5 toys. How many fewer toys does Ronald have than Marcel? $3 + \blacksquare = 5, 5 - 3 = \blacksquare$ Example from Lesson 7.1, Problem 2 • Additional Lessons 7.4, 7.6, 7.7
	BIGGER UNKNOWN	INTO MATH EXAMPLES
	Version 1 The **smaller quantity** is known along with the **difference** between the smaller quantity and the unknown **greater quantity**. The problem is stated so that the unknown quantity is described as "greater than" the known quantity.	Lucille has 5 yo-yos. Lester has 4 more yo-yos than Lucille. How many yo-yos does Lester have? $5 + 4 = \blacksquare$ Example from Lesson 7.2, Task 1 • Additional Lessons 7.5, 7.6, 7.7, 13.6
	Version 2 The **smaller quantity** is known along with the **difference** between the smaller quantity and the unknown **greater quantity**. The problem is stated so that the unknown quantity is described as "less than" or "fewer than" the known quantity.	Mike has 7 dolls. Mike has 3 fewer dolls than Elana. How many dolls does Elana have? $7 + 3 = \blacksquare$ Example from Lesson 7.2, Task 2 • Additional Lessons 7.5, 7.6, 7.7

Problem type continued on next page →

Problem Types

	SMALLER UNKNOWN	*INTO MATH* EXAMPLES
COMPARE	*Version 1* The **larger quantity** is known along with the **difference** between the larger quantity and the unknown **smaller quantity**. The problem is stated so that the known quantity is described as "more than" the unknown quantity.	Eddie wins 6 tokens in a game. Eddie wins 4 more tokens than Gorgio. How many tokens does Gorgio win? $6 - 4 = \blacksquare, \blacksquare + 4 = 6$ Example from Lesson 7.3, Problem 4 · Additional Lessons 7.5, 7.6, 7.7, 13.4
	Version 2 The **larger quantity** is known along with the **difference** between the larger quantity and the unknown **smaller quantity**. The problem is stated so that the unknown quantity is described as "fewer/less than" the known quantity.	Danny has 5 crayons. Suki has 3 fewer crayons than Danny. How many crayons does Suki have? $5 - 3 = \blacksquare, \blacksquare + 3 = 5$ Example from Lesson 7.3, Problem 3 · Additional Lessons 7.5, 7.6, 7.7, 13.4

Notes & Reflections

_____

_____

_____

_____

_____

_____

_____

_____

_____

_____

_____

_____

_____

_____

_____

_____

_____

_____

Differentiated Support Using *Do The Math*

Do The Math can be implemented with *Into Math* core instruction during the Differentiated Options block or as a separate instruction block. Depending on student level, *Do The Math* instruction can be provided as Tier 1, 2, or 3 support.

Do The Math as Tier 1 Support *Do The Math* Addition & Subtraction modules provide Tier 1 supports for the following **Grade 1** skills as shown in the table below.

Grade 1 Skills	Addition & Subtraction Modules			
	Number Core	A	B	C
Fluently add within 10.	X	X		X
Relate counting to addition and subtraction.	X			
Determine the unknown whole number in an addition equation relating to three whole numbers.	X			X
Use addition within 20 to solve word problems involving situations of adding to, taking from, putting together, taking apart, and comparing, with unknowns in all positions.	X	X		
Understand subtraction as an unknown-addend problem.	X			
Fluently subtract within 10.	X			
Use subtraction within 20 to solve word problems involving situations of adding to, taking from, putting together, taking apart, and comparing, with unknowns in all positions.	X		X	
Understand that the numbers from 11 to 19 are composed of a ten and ones.	X			
Add within 20.	X	X		
Subtract within 20.	X		X	
Understand that the two digits of a two-digit number represent amounts of tens and ones.	X	X		
Understand that 10 can be thought of as a bundle of ten ones – called a "ten".	X	X		X
Understand that the numbers 10, 20, 30, 40, 50, 60, 70, 80, 90 refer to one, two, three, four, five, six, seven, eight, or nine tens.	X	X		
Decompose two-digit numbers in multiple ways (e.g., 64 can be decomposed into 6 tens and 4 ones or into 5 tens and 14 ones).	X	X		X
Understand subtraction as an unknown-addend problem.	X		X	
Use subtraction within 20 to solve word problems involving situations of adding to, taking from, putting together, taking apart, and comparing, with unknowns in all positions.	X		X	
Determine if equations involving subtraction are true or false.			X	
Compare two two-digit numbers based on meanings of the tens and ones digits, recording the results of comparisons with the symbols >, =, and <.			X	
Understand that in adding two-digit numbers, one adds tens and tens, ones and ones; and sometimes it is necessary to compose a ten.				X
Apply properties of operations as strategies to add and subtract.				X
Add within 100, including adding a two-digit number and a multiple of 10, using a variety of strategies.				X
Determine if equations involving addition are true or false.				X

Do The Math as Tier 2 and Tier 3 Support The following *Do The Math* Addition & Subtraction modules reinforce the Kindergarten skills, and may be used to provide Tier 2 and Tier 3 supports in **Grade 1**.

Kindergarten Skills	Addition & Subtraction Modules Number Core	A	B	C
Understand addition as joining.	X			
Represent addition with objects, fingers, mental images, drawings, sounds (e.g., claps), acting out situations, verbal explanations, expressions, or equations.	X	X		
Record each composition for a number from 11 to 19 from ones by a drawing or equation (e.g., $18 = 10 + 8$).	X			
For any number from 1 to 9, find the number that makes 10 when added to the given number.	X	X		
Fluently add within 5.	X			
Compose numbers from 11 to 19 from ten ones and some further ones.	X	X		
Understand that 10 ones is 1 ten.	X	X		
Add within 10.	X	X		
Solve addition word problems within 10.	X	X		
Understand subtraction as taking away.	X			
Represent subtraction with objects, fingers, mental image, drawings, sounds (e.g., claps), acting out situations, verbal explanations, expressions, or equations.	X			
Fluently subtract within 5.	X			
Subtract within 10.	X			
Solve subtraction word problems with 10.	X			

Teacher Notes

Notes & Reflections

_____

_____

_____

_____

_____

_____

_____

_____

_____

_____

_____

_____

_____

_____

_____

_____

_____

Manipulatives and Tools

Into Math provides opportunities for students to choose manipulatives and tools to help them make sense of mathematics and connect to mathematical representations. Giving students the opportunity to choose a manipulative or tool for a task provides a teacher insight into students' understanding of connections they are making with prior learning.

The tables below will help you plan which manipulatives and tools to have available for students during lesson instruction.

● Manipulative Kit   ● Basic Manipulative Kit   ● Teacher Resource Masters

Module	Manipulatives and Tools by Lesson
Module 1: Addition Strategies	● ● **connecting cubes** Lessons 1.1-1.3, 1.5–1.7 ● **Ten Frames** Lessons 1.3–1.4 ● ● **two–color counters** Lessons 1.1–1.7
Module 2: Subtraction Strategies	● ● **connecting cubes** Lessons 2.1–2.5 ● **number cubes** Lesson 2.5 ● **Ten Frames** Lessons 2.5–2.6 ● ● **two–color counters** Lessons 2.1–2.6
Module 3: Properties of Operations	● **square tiles** Lessons 3.2–3.4 ● ● **connecting cubes** Lessons 3.1–3.6 ● ● **two–color counters** Lessons 3.1–3.4, 3.6
Module 4: Apply the Addition and Subtraction Relationship	● ● **connecting cubes** Lessons 4.1–4.5 ● ● **two–color counters** Lessons 4.1–4.5
Module 5: Understand Add To and Take From Problems	● ● **connecting cubes** Lessons 5.1–5.3 ● **number cubes** Lesson 5.1 ● **Ten Frames** Lessons 5.2–5.3 ● ● **two–color counters** Lessons 5.1–5.3
Module 6: Understand Put Together and Take Apart Problems	● ● **connecting cubes** Lessons 6.1–6.5, 6.7 ● **number cubes** Lesson 6.5 ● **Ten Frames** Lesson 6.1 ● ● **two–color counters** Lessons 6.1–6.5, 6.7
Module 7: Understand Compare Problems	● ● **connecting cubes** Lessons 7.1-7.5, 7.7 ● ● **two–color counters** Lessons 7.1-7.5, 7.7

Manipulatives and Tools

● Manipulative Kit   ● Basic Manipulative Kit   ● Teacher Resource Masters

Module	Manipulatives and Tools by Lesson
Module 8: Data	●● **connecting cubes** Lessons 8.1, 8.3–8.6 ● **plane shapes** Lesson 8.2 ●● **two–color counters** Lesson 8.3
Module 9: Understand Place Value	●● **connecting cubes** Lessons 9.1–9.3 ● **Hundred Chart** Lesson 9.3 ● **Ten Frames** Lessons 9.1–9.3 ●● **two–color counters** Lessons 9.1–9.3
Module 10: Count and Represent Numbers	●● **base–ten blocks (ones, tens)** Lessons 10.2–10.6 ●● **connecting cubes** Lessons 10.1-10.4, 10.6 ● **Counting Chart** Lessons 10.1, 10.5–10.6 ● **number cubes** Lesson 10.1 ● **Place-Value Charts** Lessons 10.2–10.5
Module 11: Compare Numbers	●● **base–ten blocks (ones, tens)** Lessons 11.1–11.3 ● **Hundred Chart** Lesson 11.3 ● **Number Line (Blank)** Lesson 11.3 ● **Place-Value Charts** Lessons 11.1–11.2
Module 12: Understand Addition and Subtraction with Tens and Ones	●● **base–ten blocks (ones, tens)** Lessons 12.1–12.8 ●● **connecting cubes** Lessons 12.1–12.3 ● **number cubes** Lessons 12.1, 12.6
Module 13: Two–Digit Addition and Subtraction	●● **base–ten blocks (ones, tens)** Lessons 13.1–13.4 ● **Hundred Chart** Lessons 13.1–13.2 ● **Place–Value Charts** Lesson 13.4
Module 14: Three-Dimensional Shapes	● **Cone Pattern** Lesson 14.1 ● **Cube Pattern** Lesson 14.1 ● **Cylinder Pattern** Lesson 14.1 ● **Rectangular Prism Pattern** Lesson 14.1 ● **three–dimensional shapes** Lessons 14.1–14.3
Module 15: Two–Dimensional Shapes	● **1–inch Grid Paper** Lesson 15.5 ● **pattern blocks** Lessons 15.1–15.5 ● **plane shapes** Lessons 15.1–15.4 ● **three–dimensional shapes** Lesson 15.2 ● **Two-Dimensional Shapes** Lesson 15.4 ● **Two-Dimensional Shapes (to combine)** Lesson 15.4 ● **Two-Dimensional Shape Cards** Lesson 15.1

Manipulatives and Tools

● Manipulative Kit   ● Basic Manipulative Kit   ● Teacher Resource Masters

Module	Manipulatives and Tools by Lesson
Module 16: Fraction Foundations	● **Circles (different sizes)** Lesson 16.4 ● **Equal and Unequal Shares Cards** Lesson 16.2 ● **pattern blocks** Lesson 16.1 ● **plane shapes** Lesson 16.1 ● **Rectangles** Lesson 16.4 ● **Squares** Lesson 16.4 ● **Two–Dimensional Shapes** Lesson 16.3
Module 17: Measure Length	● **1-inch Grid Paper** Lesson 17.4 ●● **base-ten blocks (ones)** Lessons 17.3–17.4 ● **square tiles** Lessons 17.3–17.4
Module 18: Measure Time	● **Analog Clock Model** Lesson 18.3 ● **Time Cards** Lesson 18.2

Teacher Notes

Notes & Reflections

Unit 1 Performance Assessment

Let's Help Chen Add and Subtract!

Task Summary The Unit 1 Performance Assessment will have students:

- Add three whole numbers whose sum is less than or equal to 20.
- Apply properties of operations as strategies to add and subtract.
- Add and subtract within 20.
- Determine the unknown whole number in an addition or subtraction equation relating to three whole numbers.

Name _____   Unit 1
                                                  Performance Task

Let's Help Chen Add and Subtract!

Chen uses different strategies to add and subtract. He works with the addends 4, 5, 6, and 7.

1 Choose one of Chen's addends. Use that number to write a doubles fact. Use pictures and numbers to explain.
Possible answer:

___4___ + ___4___ = ___8___

Check children's explanation.

2 Add two of Chen's numbers. Then add the same numbers in a different order.
Possible answer:

___5___ + ___6___ = ___11___

___6___ + ___5___ = ___11___

Grade 1 • Unit 1 • Performance Task   103

Unit 1
Performance Task   Name _____

3 Add three of Chen's numbers. Circle the two numbers you add first. Explain why you chose those numbers.
Possible answer:

___4___ + ___5___ + ___6___ = ___15___

Check children's explanation. _____

_____

_____

4 Use one of Chen's numbers to complete the subtraction sentence. Use the ten frame to show your work.

11 − ___5___ = 6   Check children's work.

104

If students encounter difficulties in completing any of the tasks, use the information below to aid in interpreting student performance and to identify suggestions for follow-up and intervention.

Item	Content Focus	DOK	Intervene with
1	Add within 20 using doubles.	2	Reteach 1.5
2	Apply the Commutative property of addition.	2	Reteach 3.1 Reteach 3.2
3	Add three whole numbers whose sum is less than or equal to 20.	2	Reteach 3.3 Reteach 3.4
4	Subtract within 20.	2	Reteach 2.5

Additional teacher support and a scoring rubric can be found in your Assessment Guide.

Unit 2 Performance Assessment

Colors and Flavors

Task Summary The Unit 2 Performance Assessment will have students:

- Organize, represent, and interpret data with up to three categories.
- Use addition and subtraction within 20 to solve word problems.

Name _____

Colors and Flavors

Ani asked 15 children which color they liked best: red, blue, or purple. The most children chose blue. The fewest children chose red.

1 Make a tally chart to show the choices. Possible answer:

Favorite Color		Total
red	////	4
blue	//////	6
purple	/////	5

Now use the tally chart to answer the questions.

2 How many children chose colors? ___15___

3 How many fewer children chose red than purple? Possible answer: 1

4 How many more children chose purple than red? Possible answer: 1

108

Name _____

Twelve children bought muffins at a bake sale.
Four children chose apple muffins.
Two more children chose blueberry than apple.
The rest chose banana.

5 Make a bar graph about the muffins.

Muffins Children Chose

Muffins	
apple	
blueberry	
banana	

0 1 2 3 4 5 6 7 8 9 10
Number of Children

Now use the graph to answer the questions.

6 What kind of muffin did the most children choose?

blueberry muffins

7 What kind of muffin was chosen by the fewest children?

banana muffins

8 How many children in all chose apple or banana?

6

Grade 1 • Unit 2 • Performance Task   109

If students encounter difficulties in completing any of the tasks, use the information below to aid in interpreting student performance and to identify suggestions for follow-up and intervention.

Item	Content Focus	DOK	Intervene with
1	Represent data on a tally chart.	2	Reteach 8.3 Reteach 8.4
2	Use addition within 20 to solve word problems.	1	Reteach 6.1 Reteach 6.6
3	Use addition and subtraction within 20 to solve word problems.	2	Reteach 5.2 Reteach 5.4
4	Interpret data from a tally chart.	2	Reteach 8.3 Reteach 8.4
5–7	Interpret data from a bar graph.	2	Reteach 8.5 Reteach 8.6
8	Use addition within 20 to solve word problems.	1	Reteach 6.1 Reteach 6.6

Additional teacher support and a scoring rubric can be found in your Assessment Guide.

Unit 3 Performance Assessment

Jamal's Marbles

Task Summary The Unit 3 Performance Assessment will have students:

- Compare two two-digit numbers using the symbols >, =, and <.
- Mentally find 10 more or 10 less than a two-digit number; explain the reasoning used.
- Count to 120, starting at any number less than 120.
- Understand that the two digits of a two-digit number represent amounts of tens and ones.

Name _____

Unit 3
Performance Task

Jamal's Marbles

Jamal has some marbles.
He has 28 green marbles.

1 If the number of red marbles is 10 less than the number of green marbles, how many red marbles does Jamal have? ___18___

Write how you know.

Check children's explanations.
_____

2 If the number of blue marbles is 10 more than the number of green marbles, how many blue marbles does Jamal have? ___38___

Write how you know.

Check children's explanations.
_____

3 If the number of yellow marbles is 10 less than the number of blue marbles, how many yellow marbles does Jamal have? ___28___

Write how you know.

Check children's explanations.
_____

Grade 1 • Unit 3 • Performance Task   113

Unit 3
Performance Task

Name _____

Use ▭▭▭ and ▫.
Write the number for each color of Jamal's marbles.

Compare the tens. Compare the ones.
Then write >, <, or = to complete the sentence.

4 ___18___ (<) ___28___
   red   yellow

5 ___28___ (=) ___28___
   yellow   green

6 ___38___ (>) ___18___
   blue   red

If Jamal has 112 marbles, how many more marbles does he need to have 120? Write how you know.
(Hint: Start at 112 and count up to help you solve.)

8; Check children's explanations.
_____

114

If students encounter difficulties in completing any of the tasks, use the information below to aid in interpreting student performance and to identify suggestions for follow-up and intervention.

Item	Content Focus	DOK	Intervene with
1	Mentally find 10 more or 10 less than a given two-digit number.	2	Reteach 11.2
2	Mentally find 10 more or 10 less than a given two-digit number.	2	Reteach 11.1
3	Mentally find 10 more or 10 less than a given two-digit number.	2	Reteach 11.2
4	Compare two two-digit numbers using >, =, or <.	1	Reteach 11.3
5	Compare two two-digit numbers using >, =, or <.	1	Reteach 11.3
6	Count to 120, starting at any number less than 120.	1	Reteach 10.1

Additional teacher support and a scoring rubric can be found in your Assessment Guide.

Unit 4 Performance Assessment

So Many Markers!

Task Summary The Unit 4 Performance Assessment will have students:

- Add within 100, including adding a two-digit number and a one-digit number, and adding a two-digit number and a multiple of 10, using drawings and strategies based on place value, properties of operations, and/or the relationship between addition and subtraction.

- Relate counting to addition and subtraction.
- Subtract multiples of 10 in the range 10–90 from multiples of 10 in the range 10–90, using drawings and strategies based on place value, properties of operations, and/or the relationship between addition and subtraction.

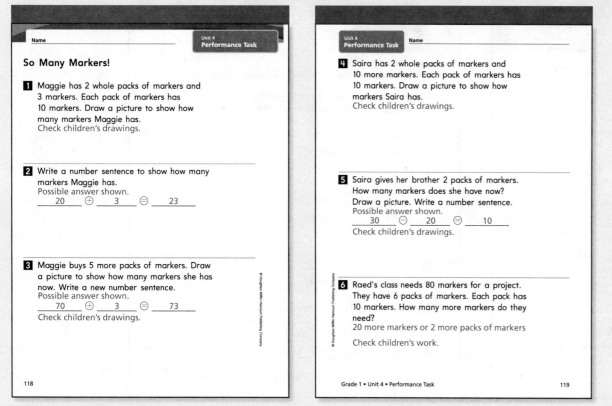

If students encounter difficulties in completing any of the tasks, use the information below to aid in interpreting student performance and to identify suggestions for follow-up and intervention.

Item	Content Focus	DOK	Intervene with
1	Add a one-digit number to a two-digit number within 100.	2	Reteach 12.6 Reteach 12.7
2	Add within 100.	2	Reteach 13.1 Reteach 13.2 Reteach 13.4
3	Add within 100.	2	Reteach 12.3
4	Add within 100.	2	Reteach 12.6 Reteach 12.7
5	Subtract multiples of 10 from multiples of 10 in the range of 10–90.	2	Reteach 13.3
6	Subtract multiples of 10 from multiples of 10 in the range of 10–90.	2	Reteach 13.1 Reteach 13.3

Additional teacher support and a scoring rubric can be found in your Assessment Guide.

Unit 5 Performance Assessment

Shape Up!

Task Summary The Unit 5 Performance Assessment will have students:

- Distinguish between defining attributes versus non-defining attributes; build and draw shapes that possess defining attributes.
- Compose two-dimensional shapes or three-dimensional shapes to create a composite shape, and compose new shapes from the composite shape.
- Partition circles and rectangles into two and four equal shares; describe the shares using the words *halves, fourths,* and *quarters*; and use the phrases *half of, fourth of,* and *quarter of*. Describe the whole as two of or four of the shares.

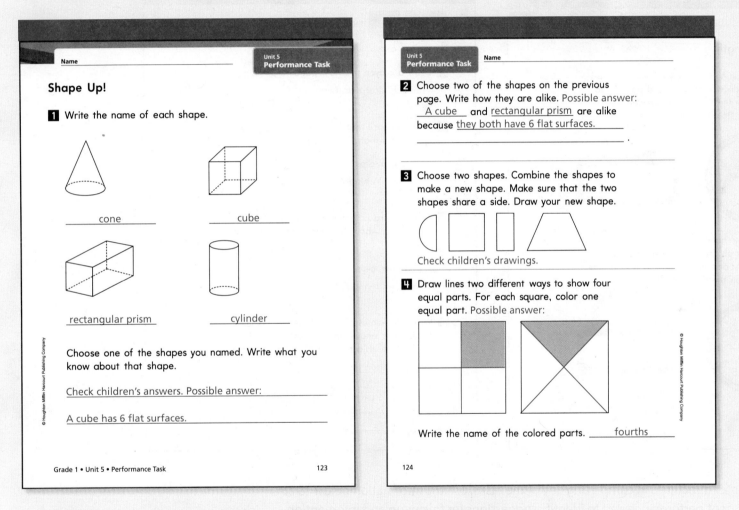

If students encounter difficulties in completing any of the tasks, use the information below to aid in interpreting student performance and to identify suggestions for follow-up and intervention.

Item	Content Focus	DOK	Intervene with
1	Identify three-dimensional shapes using defining attributes.	2	Reteach 14.1
2	Describe defining attributes of three-dimensional shapes.	2	Reteach 14.1
3	Combine two-dimensional shapes to create a composite shape.	2	Reteach 15.3 Reteach 15.4
4	Partition rectangles into four equal shares, and describe the shares using the words *fourths* and *quarters*.	2	Reteach 16.4

Additional teacher support and a scoring rubric can be found in your Assessment Guide.

Unit 6 Performance Assessment

Time and Length

Task Summary The Unit 6 Performance Assessment will have students:

- Order three objects by length; compare the lengths of two objects indirectly by using a third object.
- Express the length of an object as a whole number of length units, by laying multiple copies of a shorter object (the length unit) end to end.
- Tell and write time in hours and half hours using analog and digital clocks.

Time and Length

1 Draw an hour hand on any number on the clock. Then draw a minute hand pointing to the 12. Write the time in numbers on the digital clock. Possible answers are shown.

3:00

2 Draw an hour hand pointing between any two numbers on the clock. Then draw a minute hand pointing to the 6. Write the time in numbers on the digital clock.

Possible answers are shown.

4:30

128

Unit 6
Performance Task

Use paper clips.

3 Draw a crayon that is 4 paper clips long.

Check children's drawings.

4 Draw a pencil that is longer than the crayon. About how many paper clips long is it?

_____ paper clips

Check children's drawings.

5 Draw a third object that is shorter than the crayon. About how many paper clips long is it?

_____ paper clips

Check children's drawings.

6 Write the names of your three objects in order from longest to shortest. How did you know which object was the longest? Explain.

Check children's work.

Grade 1 • Unit 6 • Performance Task

129

If students encounter difficulties in completing any of the tasks, use the information below to aid in interpreting student performance and to identify suggestions for follow-up and intervention.

Item	Content Focus	DOK	Intervene with
1	Tell and write time in hours and half hours using analog and digital clocks.	1	Reteach 18.4
2	Tell and write time in hours and half hours using analog and digital clocks.	1	Reteach 18.4
3–6	Order and compare objects by length.	2	Reteach 17.1 Reteach 17.3

Additional teacher support and a scoring rubric can be found in your Assessment Guide.

Notes & Reflections

Into Math Solutions and Components

Core Materials

Student Materials

ONLINE
- Access all program materials
- Complete and submit assignments and assessments
- Assign Interactive Practice with Hints, Corrective Feedback, and Try Again support
- Track progress

Student Edition*

Multi-volume: write-in, consumable

Practice and Homework Journal*

One volume: write-in, consumable

Teacher Materials

ONLINE
- Access all program materials
- Plan lessons
- Assign materials
- View reports
- Group students and get recommendations
- Access immediate scores / item analysis
- Access reports on standards and skills

Teacher Edition

Conveniently sized for at-home planning

Planning and Pacing Guide

Correlations, resources, and pacing

Module Support Videos

Classroom videos featuring learning tasks, Language Routines, Talk Moves, and differentiation

Assessments

ONLINE
- Access and assign Math Growth Measure interim assessment
- Access and assign digital assessments and reports

Assessment Guide*

Secure assessment masters for teachers, including Form A and Form B for every module

Getting Ready for High Stakes Assessment*

High Stakes Assessment readiness practice for every Math Standard, with three half-length Practice Tests

*All print and digital student-facing materials are available in Spanish.

Differentiation and Support Materials

Digital and interactive versions of resources are available on Ed: Your Friend in Learning.

ONLINE

- Math Center Activities
- Fluency Checks
- Digital Readers
- Poggles Digital Game
- Multilingual Glossary
- Digital Toolbox
- Math on the Spot tutorial videos
- School Home Letters

MathBoard
Write-on / wipe-off

Readers
With Lexile® scores

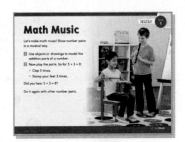

Unit Project Cards
Featuring STEM and careers

ONLINE

- Math Center Activities
- Interactive Reteach, Challenge, Additional Practice and RtI
- Interactive Fluency Checks
- Digital Readers
- Poggles Digital Game
- Getting Ready for High Stakes Assessment Checks
- MTSS/RtI Tier 2 and Tier 3 Materials

Differentiated Instruction*
Reteach, Challenge, Additional Practice, Fluency

Tabletop Flipchart
Mini-lessons for reteaching to targeted small groups

Vocabulary Cards and Games*
Meaningful and fun activities

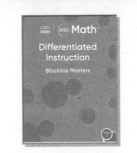

Classroom Manipulatives Kit
Hands-on materials

Differentiated Centers
Math Center organizers

Professional Learning and Implementation Support

ONLINE

- Getting Started Module
- Professional Learning Guide provided during implementation training

Professional Learning Cards
Feature Talk Moves and Language Routines

Getting Started Module and Professional Learning Guide
Implementation support

Academic Notebooks and Math Journals

Into Math has a variety of options to help students summarize learning. The Practice and Homework Journal includes several page types that students can add to Academic Notebooks or Math Journals.

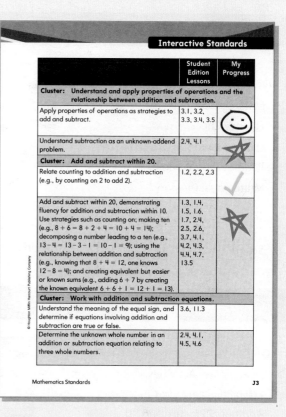

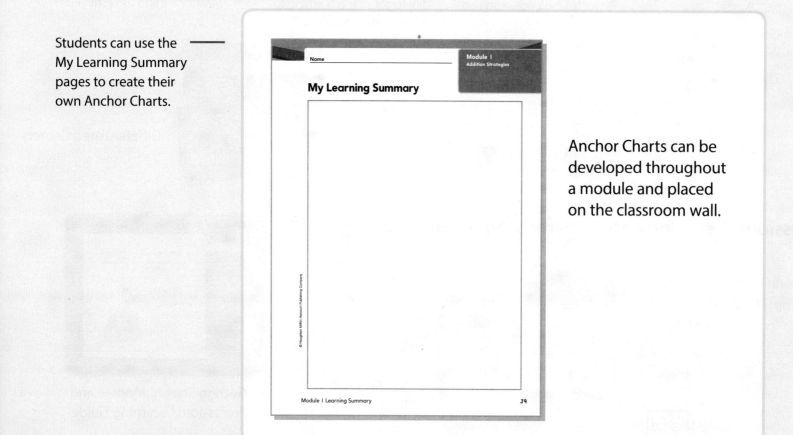

Students should add to their Interactive Glossary throughout the year as they develop understanding for each term. See the complete Interactive Glossary on pp. PG112–PG122.

Use the Interactive Standards Chart to record mastery of each standard.

Students can use the My Learning Summary pages to create their own Anchor Charts.

Anchor Charts can be developed throughout a module and placed on the classroom wall.

Strategies for Addition

Use Pictures and Equations to Represent Addition

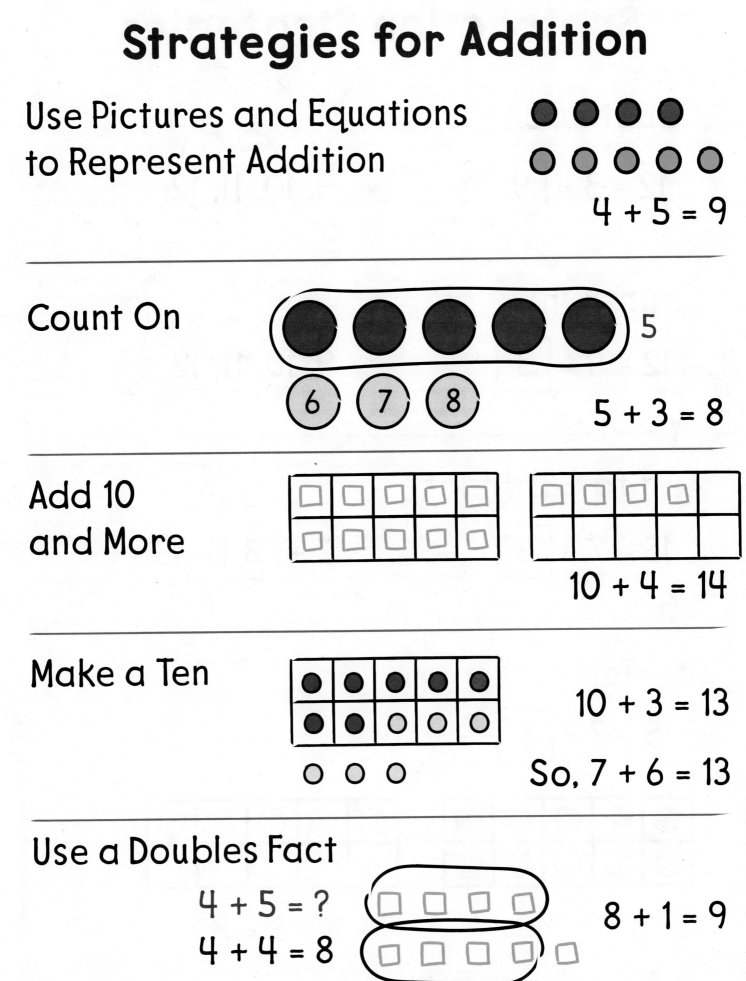

$4 + 5 = 9$

Count On

5

6 7 8

$5 + 3 = 8$

Add 10 and More

$10 + 4 = 14$

Make a Ten

$10 + 3 = 13$

So, $7 + 6 = 13$

Use a Doubles Fact

$4 + 5 = ?$

$4 + 4 = 8$

$8 + 1 = 9$

Subtraction Strategies

Count Back

12 − 3 = 9

9, 10, 11, 12

Count On

12 − 9 = 3

9, 10, 11, 12

Add to Subtract

15 − 7 = 8

7 + 8 = 15

Use Ten

15 − 7 = 8

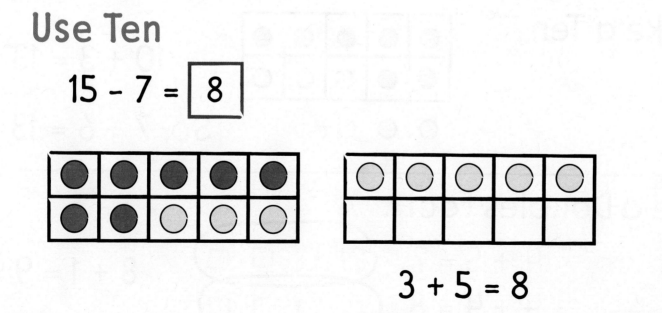

3 + 5 = 8

Properties of Operations

$$3 + 4 = 7 \text{ and } 4 + 3 = 7$$

$$3 + 7 + 2 = 12 \qquad 3 + 7 + 2 = 12$$

$$10 + 2 = 12 \qquad 3 + 9 = 12$$

$$4 + 6 = 10 \qquad \text{True}$$

$$2 + 7 = 10 \qquad \text{False}$$

How Are Addition and Subtraction Related?

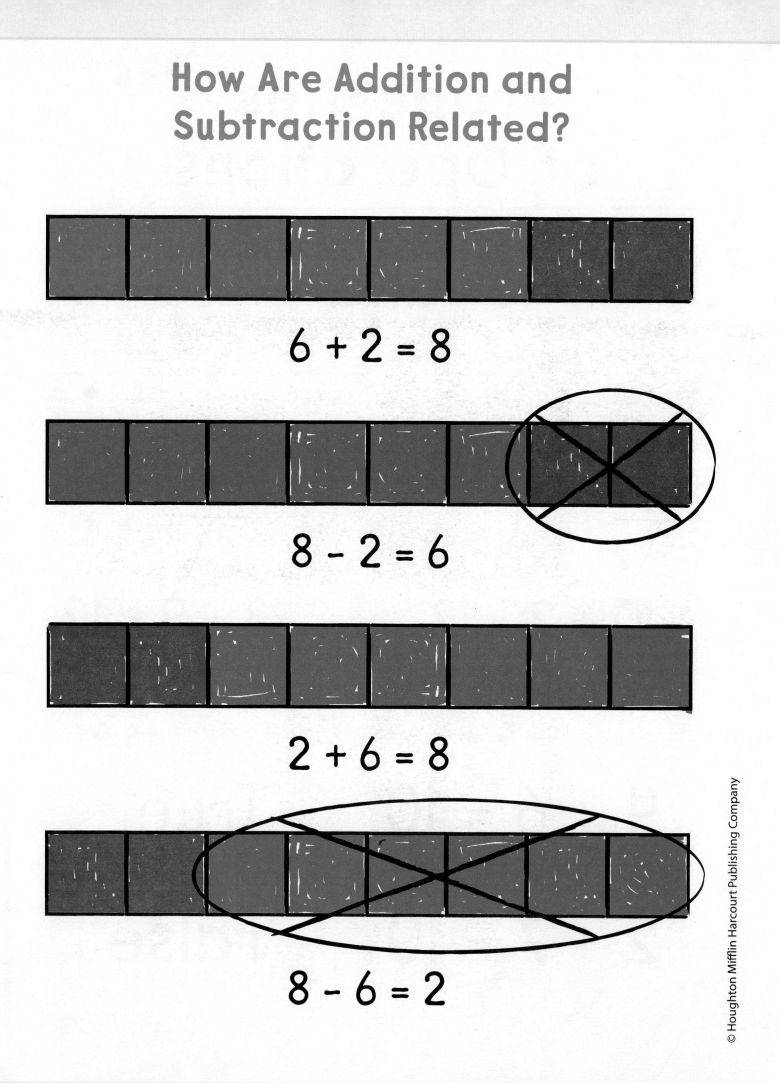

6 + 2 = 8

8 − 2 = 6

2 + 6 = 8

8 − 6 = 2

Add To and Take From: Possible Ways to Solve

Use Counters to Add

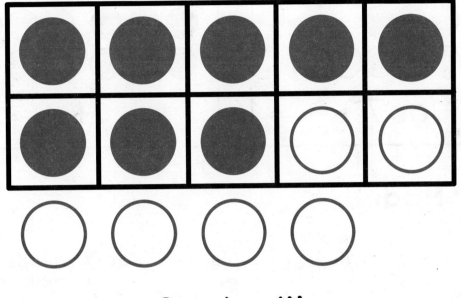

8 + 6 = 14

- -

Use Counters to Subtract

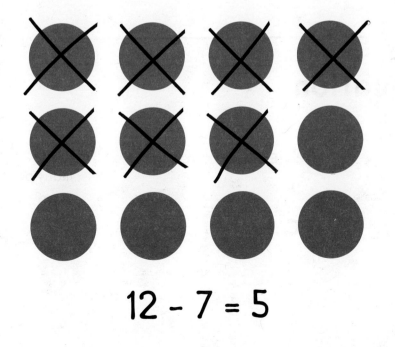

12 − 7 = 5

Put Together/Take Apart: Possible Ways to Solve

Draw a Visual Model

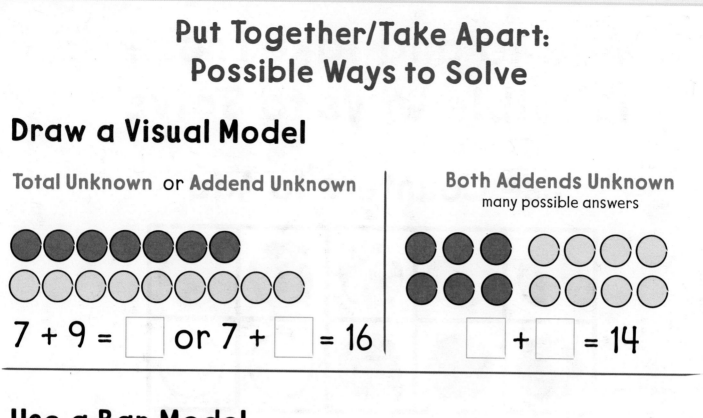

Total Unknown or **Addend Unknown**

$$7 + 9 = \boxed{} \quad \text{or} \quad 7 + \boxed{} = 16$$

Both Addends Unknown
many possible answers

$$\boxed{} + \boxed{} = 14$$

Use a Bar Model

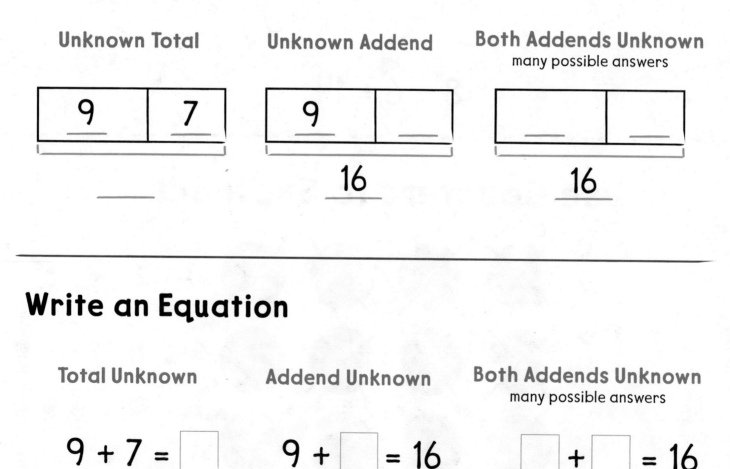

Unknown Total

9	7

_____

Unknown Addend

9	

16

Both Addends Unknown
many possible answers

16

Write an Equation

Total Unknown

$$9 + 7 = \boxed{}$$

Addend Unknown

$$9 + \boxed{} = 16$$

Both Addends Unknown
many possible answers

$$\boxed{} + \boxed{} = 16$$

Understand Compare Problems

Difference Unknown

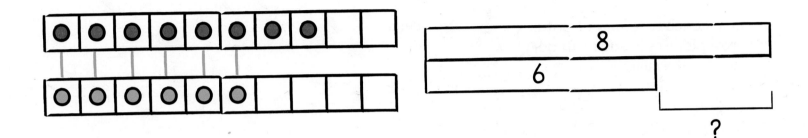

$$8 - 6 = 2$$

$$6 + 2 = 8$$

Bigger Unknown

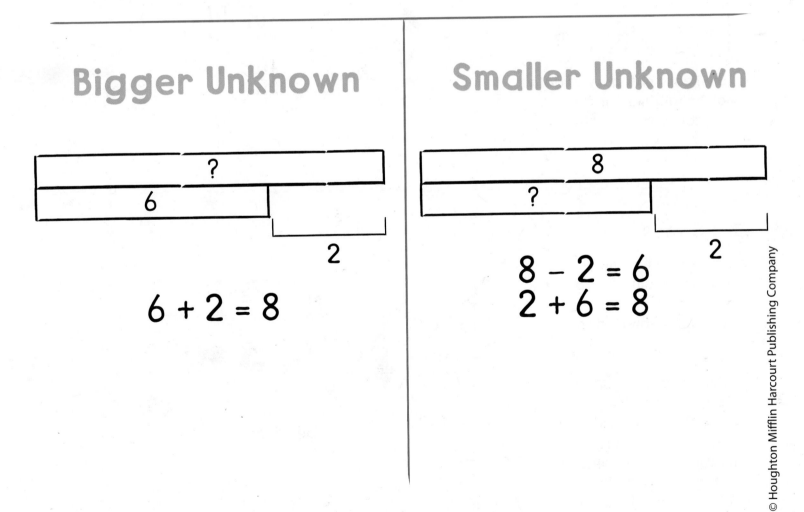

$$6 + 2 = 8$$

Smaller Unknown

$$8 - 2 = 6$$
$$2 + 6 = 8$$

Charts and Graphs

Picture Graphs

Title says what the graph is about.

Pictures show how many of each item.

Count each category of data. Draw pictures in each category to show the number of items.

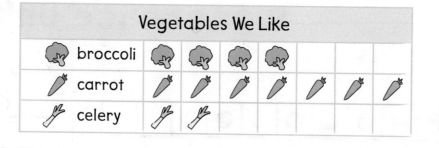

Tally Charts

Title says what the chart is about.

Tally marks show how many of each item.

| means 1. ⦀⦀ means 5.

Count each category of data. Make a tally mark in the category for each item.

Birds in the Park		Total
🐦 bluebird	‖	2
🐦 robin	⦀⦀⦀ ‖‖‖‖	9
🐦 cardinal	⦀⦀⦀	5

Bar Graphs

Title says what the graph is about.

Bars show how many of each item.

Count each category of data.
Draw the bar the right length to show the number of items in each category.

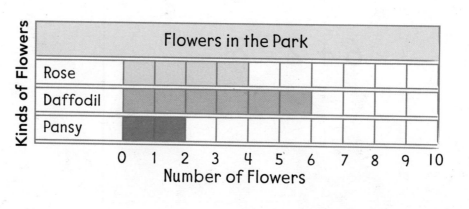

Write Numbers as Tens and Ones

16

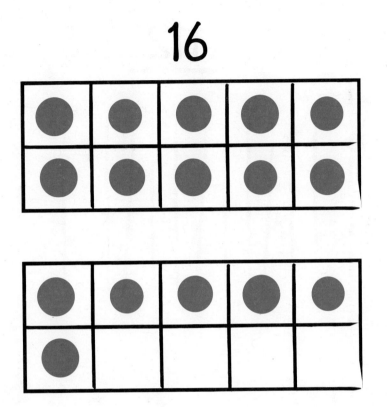

1 ten 6 ones
10 + 6
16 ones

Quick Picture

16 = | ⋮∴

60 = ||||||

Count and Represent Numbers

Counting Chart

1	2	3	4	5	6	7	8	9	10
11	12	13	14	15	16	17	18	19	20
21	22	23	24	25	26	27	28	29	30
31	32	33	34	35	36	37	38	39	40
41	42	43	44	45	46	47	48	49	50
51	52	53	54	55	56	57	58	59	60
61	62	63	64	65	66	67	68	69	70
71	72	73	74	75	76	77	78	79	80
81	82	83	84	85	86	87	88	89	90
91	92	93	94	95	96	97	98	99	100
101	102	103	104	105	106	107	108	109	110
111	112	113	114	115	116	117	118	119	120

Tens and Ones

112

Represent in Different Ways

54 = **54**

Compare Numbers

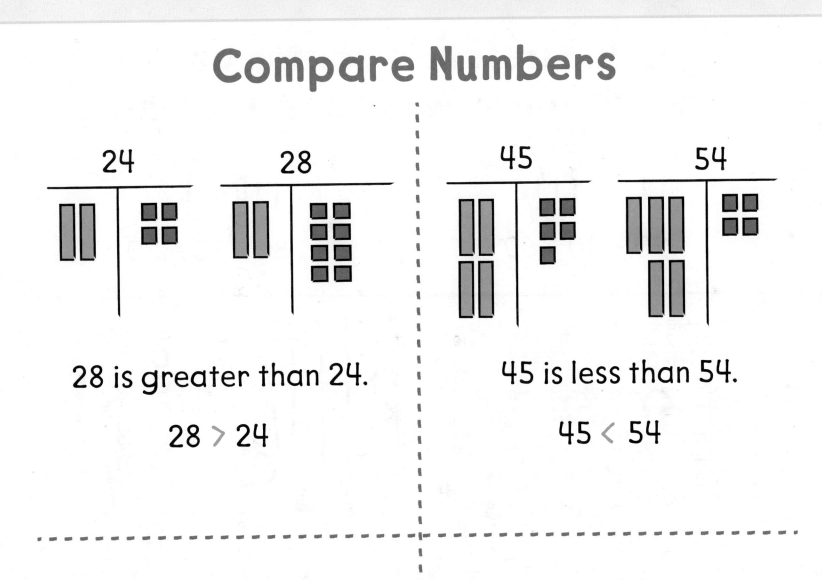

24	28

28 is greater than 24.

28 > 24

45	54

45 is less than 54.

45 < 54

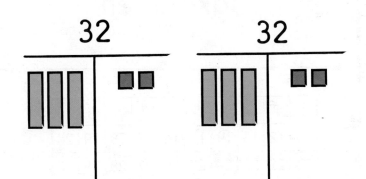

32	32

32 is equal to 32.

32 = 32

is greater than   >

is equal to   =

is less than   <

Understand Addition and Subtraction with Tens and Ones

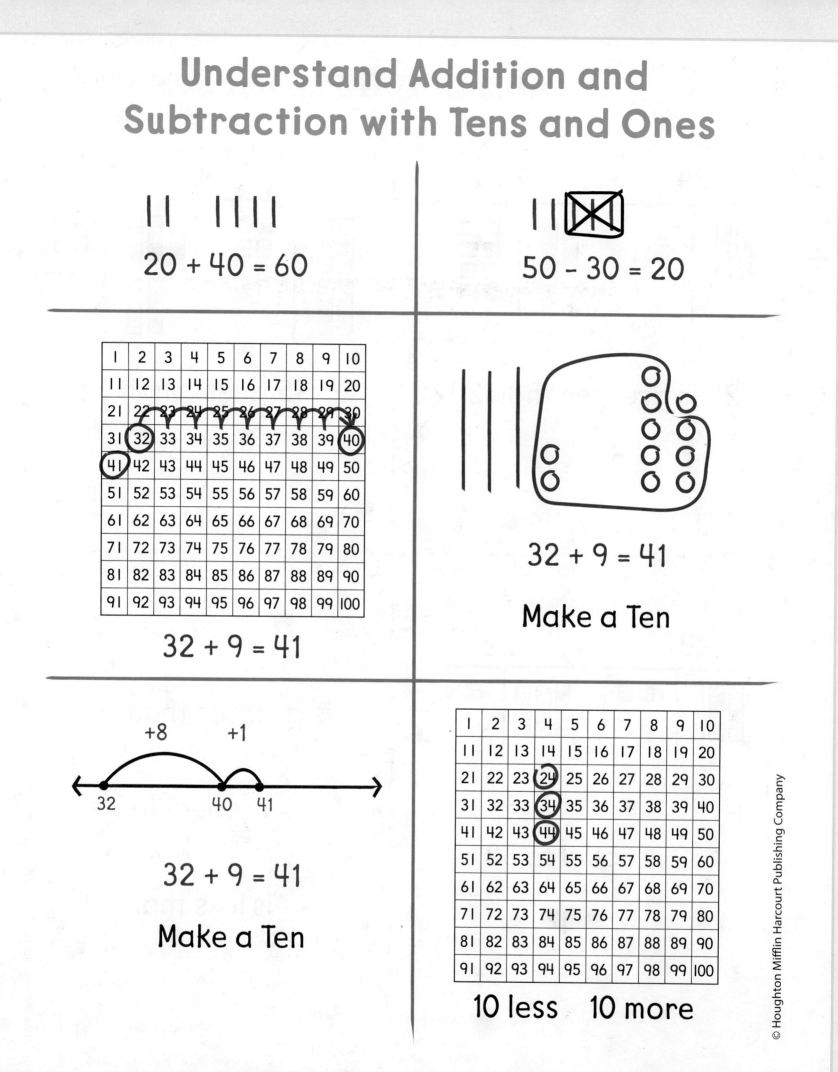

$20 + 40 = 60$

$50 - 30 = 20$

$32 + 9 = 41$

$32 + 9 = 41$

Make a Ten

+8   +1

32   40   41

$32 + 9 = 41$

Make a Ten

10 less   10 more

Two-Digit Addition and Subtraction

1	2	3	4	5	6	7	8	9	10
11	12	13	14	15	16	17	18	19	20
21	22	23	24	25	26	27	28	29	30
31	32	33	34	35	36	37	38	39	40
41	42	43	44	45	46	47	48	49	50
51	52	53	54	55	56	57	58	59	60
61	62	63	64	65	66	67	68	69	70
71	72	73	74	75	76	77	78	79	80
81	82	83	84	85	86	87	88	89	90
91	92	93	94	95	96	97	98	99	100

$$\begin{array}{r} 33 \\ +\ 20 \\ \hline 53 \end{array}$$

$$\begin{array}{r} 80 \\ -\ 30 \\ \hline 50 \end{array}$$

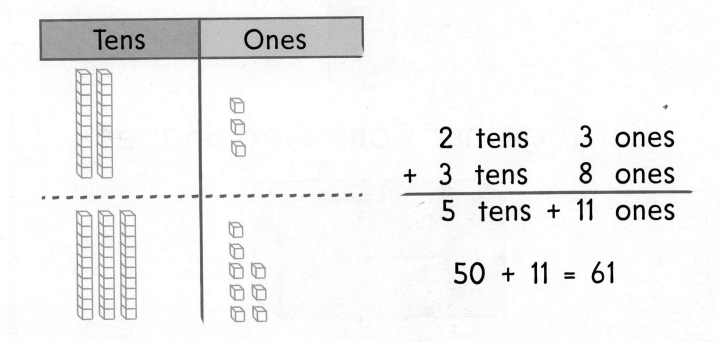

Tens	Ones

2 tens   3 ones
+ 3 tens   8 ones

5 tens + 11 ones

50 + 11 = 61

Three-Dimensional Shapes

Flat Surfaces

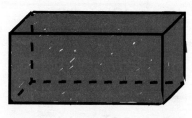

Curved Surface

Flat and Curved Surfaces

Combined Shape

Put Together Combined Shapes

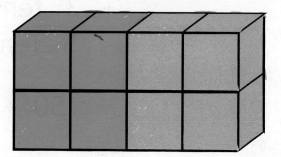

Two-Dimensional Shapes

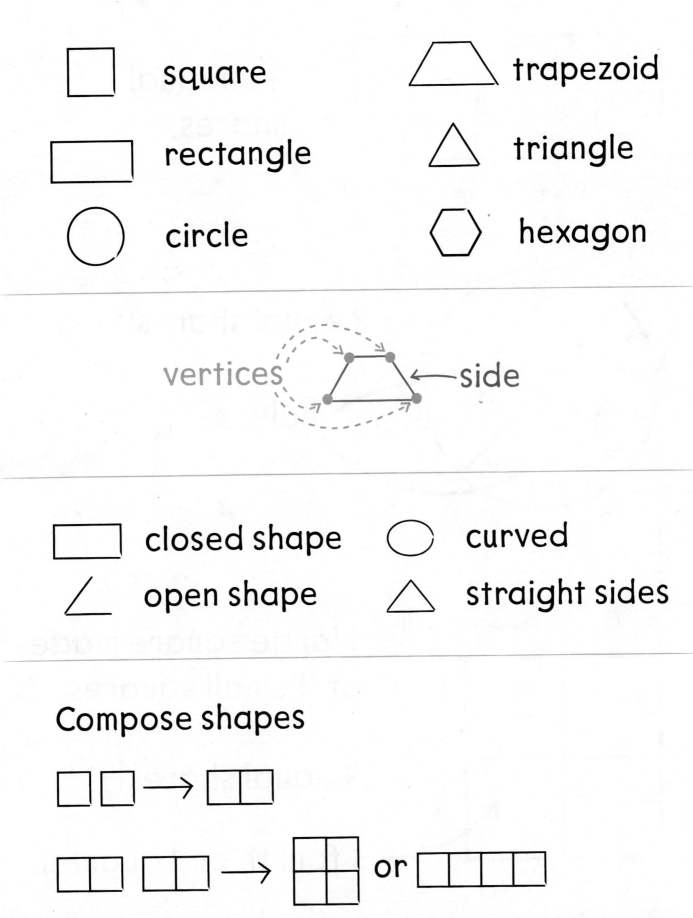

□ square

▱ trapezoid

▭ rectangle

△ triangle

○ circle

⬡ hexagon

vertices — side

▭ closed shape   ○ curved

∠ open shape   △ straight sides

Compose shapes

□ □ → ▭

▭ ▭ → ⊞ or ▭▭▭▭

Show Shares of Shapes

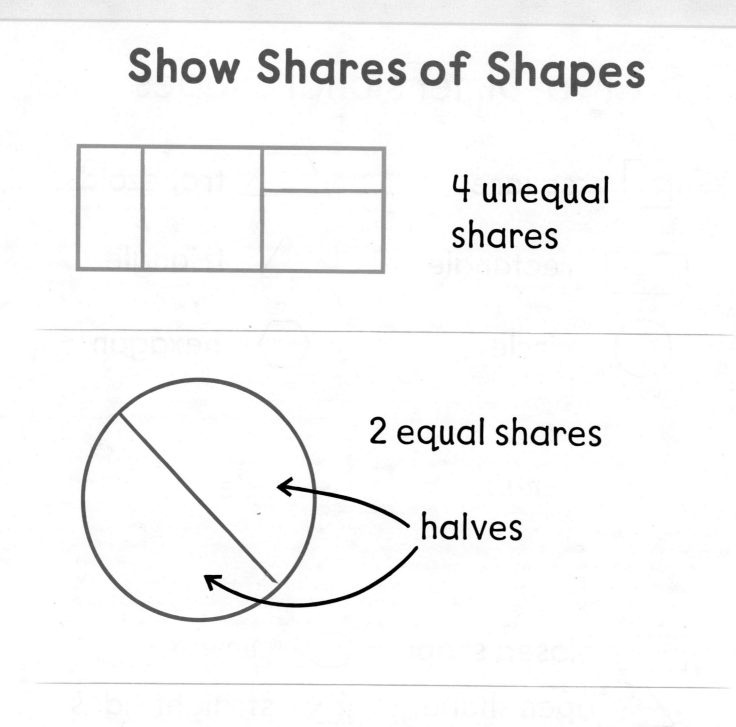

4 unequal shares

2 equal shares

halves

1 large square made of 4 small squares

4 equal shares

1 fourth or 1 quarter

Measure Length

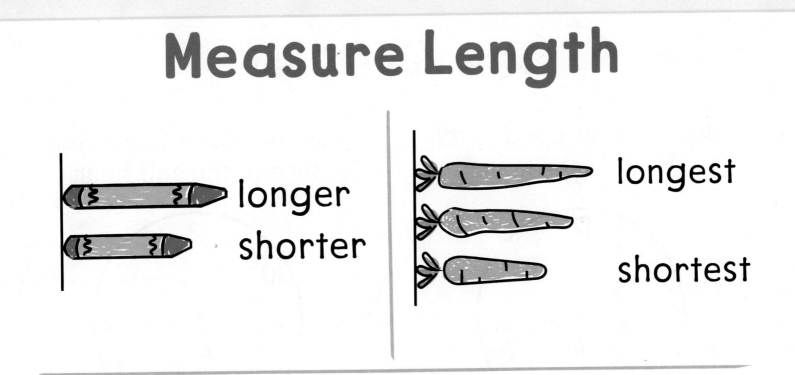

longer
shorter

longest
shortest

Measure Time

Use the hour hand to tell time to the hour.

6:00

Use the hour hand to tell time to the half hour.

6:30

Use the hour and minute hands to tell time to the hour.

4:00

Use the hour and minute hands to tell time to the half hour.

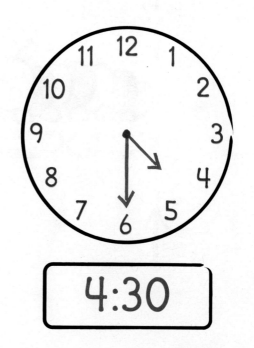

4:30

Notes & Reflections

Interactive Glossary

As you learn about each new term, add notes, drawings, or sentences in the space next to the definition. Doing so will help you remember what each term means.

Possible summaries:
My Vocabulary Summary

A

add
sumar

Add to find how many altogether.

$3 + 2 = 5$

$2 + 2 = 4$

addend
sumando

$1 + 3 = 4$

addend

$(2) + (3) = 5$

B

bar graph
gráfica de barras

Flowers in the Garden

Kind of Flower: daisies, sunflowers

Number of Flowers: 0 1 2 3 4 5 6 7

Sports We Like

Sport: soccer, basketball, football

Number of Children: 0 1 2 3 4 5 6 7 8 9 10

Interactive Glossary

Possible summaries:
My Vocabulary Summary

C

cent (¢)
centavo

A penny has a value of 1 cent (1¢).

1¢

1 cent is the value of a penny.

circle
círculo

cone
cono

has a curved surface and a flat surface

count back
contar hacia atrás

$8 - 1 = 7$

Start at 8.
Count back 1.
You are on 7.

Count back 2.

$7 - 2 = 5$

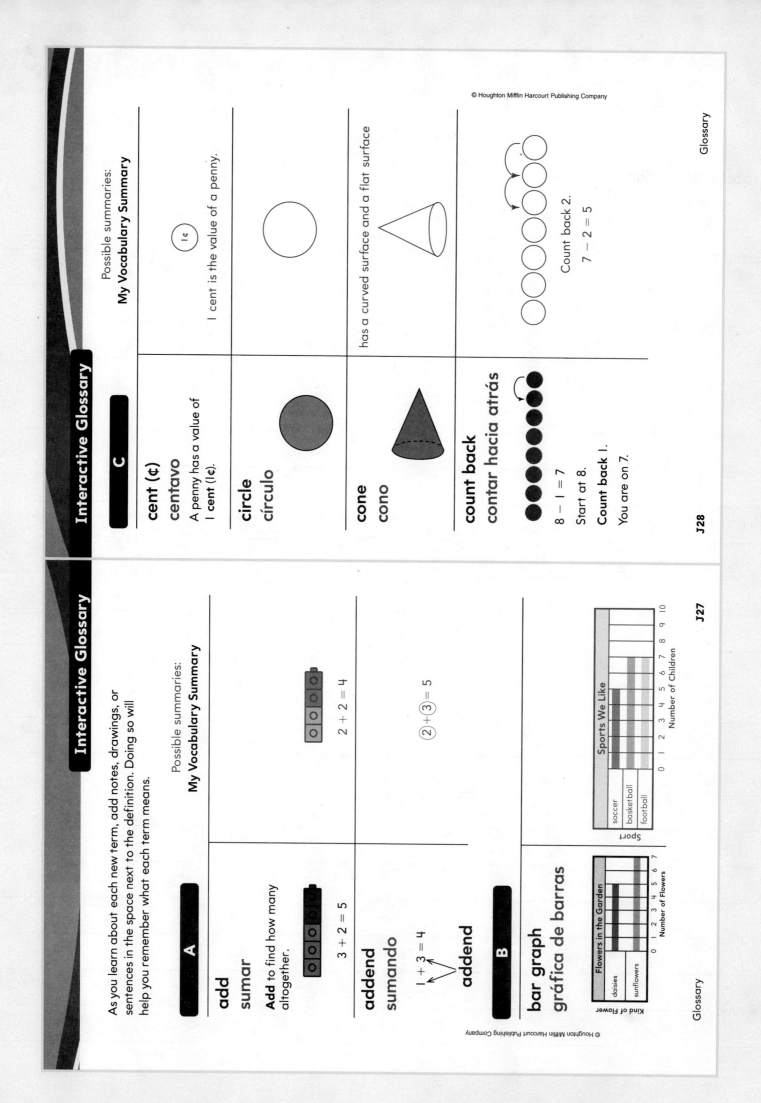

D

	Possible summaries: **My Vocabulary Summary**
difference **diferencia** $4 - 3 = 1$ The **difference** is 1.	$6 - 4 = \boxed{2}$ The difference is 2.
dime **moneda de 10¢** A dime has a value of 10 cents (10¢).	**10¢** A dime is a coin that has a value of 10 cents.
dollar **dólar** One dollar has the same value as 100 cents (100¢).	100 pennies = 100¢, or 1 dollar. 10 dimes = 100¢, or 1 dollar. 4 quarters = 100¢, or 1 dollar.

© Houghton Mifflin Harcourt Publishing Company

	Possible summaries: **My Vocabulary Summary**
count on **contar hacia** **adelante** $4 + 2 = 6$ Say 4. Count on 2. 5, 6	Count on 3 from 6. Say 7, 8, 9. $6 + 3 = 9$
cube **cubo**	has 6 flat surfaces all the same size
curved surface **superficie curva** Some three-dimensional shapes have a **curved** **surface.**	curved surface
cylinder **cilindro**	has a curved surface and 2 flat surfaces

© Houghton Mifflin Harcourt Publishing Company

Interactive Glossary

F

fewer
menos

3 fewer birds

2 fewer circles

flat surface
superficie plana

Some three-dimensional shapes have only flat surfaces.

flat surface

fourth of
cuarto de

A fourth of this shape is shaded.

This shows a fourth of a rectangle.

Possible summaries:
My Vocabulary Summary

Interactive Glossary

doubles
dobles

$5 + 5 = 10$

$4 + 4 = 8$

E

equal shares
partes iguales

These show equal parts, or **equal shares**.

equation
ecuación

$7 = 5 + 2$ is an example of an addition **equation**.

$8 - 5 = 3$ is an example of a subtraction **equation**.

Addition

$7 + 9 = 16$

Subtraction

$14 - 8 = 6$

Possible summaries:
My Vocabulary Summary

Interactive Glossary

Possible summaries:
My Vocabulary Summary

half past
y media

The time is half past 2 o'clock.

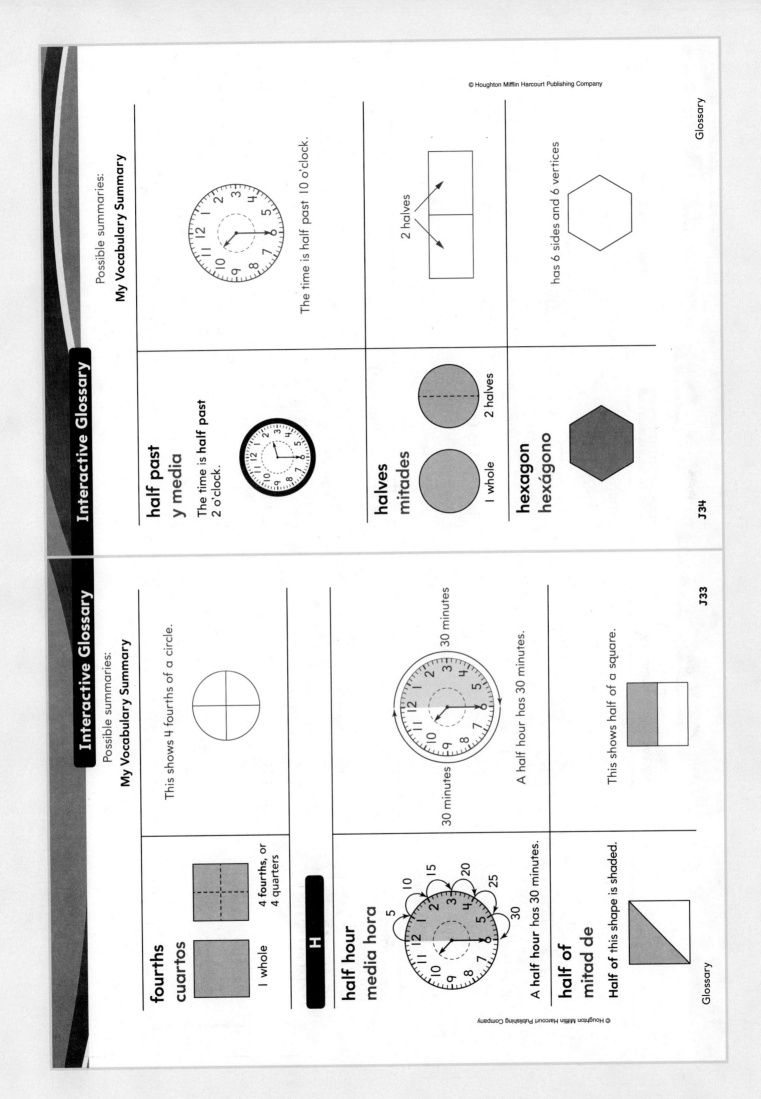

The time is half past 10 o'clock.

halves
mitades

1 whole   2 halves

hexagon
hexágono

has 6 sides and 6 vertices

Interactive Glossary

Possible summaries:
My Vocabulary Summary

fourths
cuartos

1 whole   4 fourths, or 4 quarters

This shows 4 fourths of a circle.

H

half hour
media hora

5 10 15 20 25 30

A half hour has 30 minutes.

30 minutes   30 minutes

A half hour has 30 minutes.

half of
mitad de

Half of this shape is shaded.

This shows half of a square.

Interactive Glossary

Possible summaries:
My Vocabulary Summary

I

inch
pulgada

You can use an inch to measure length.

is equal to (=)
es igual a

2 plus 1 is equal to 3.

$2 + 1 = 3$

$5 + 3 = 8$

$25 = 25$

is greater than (>)
es mayor que

35 is greater than 27.

$35 > 27$

$44 > 12$

Glossary

Interactive Glossary

Possible summaries:
My Vocabulary Summary

hour
hora

An hour has 60 minutes.

60 minutes

An hour has 60 minutes.

hour hand
horario

hour hand

The hour hand is the short hand.
It tells the hours.

Glossary

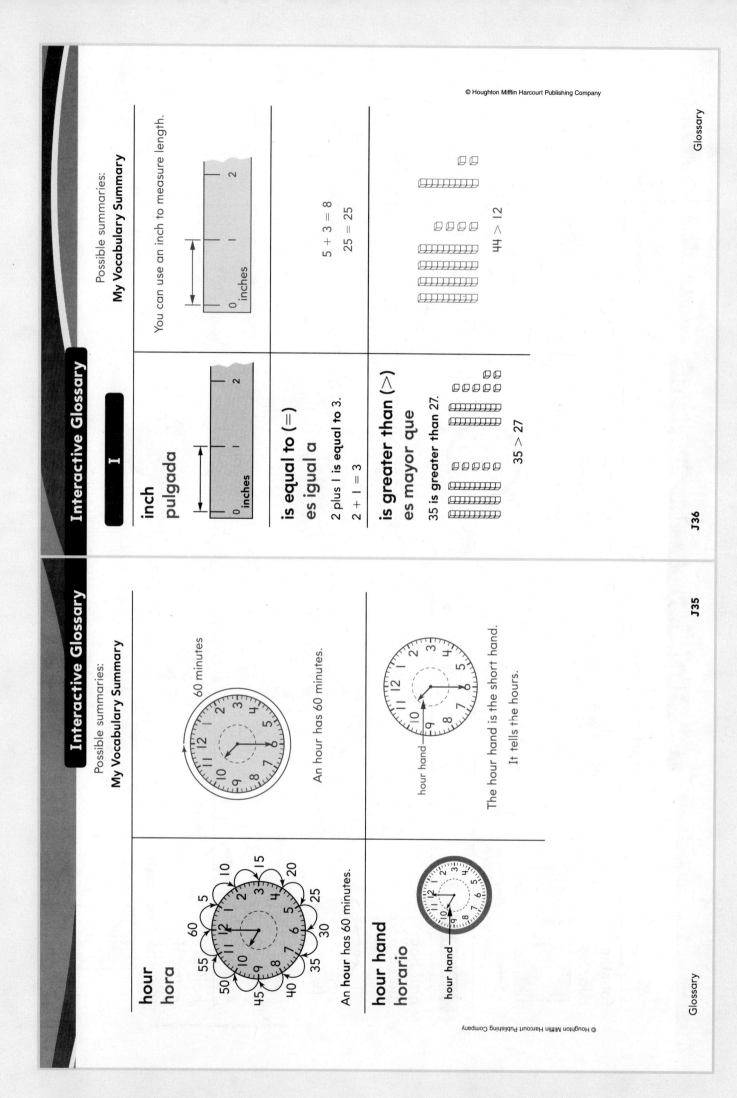

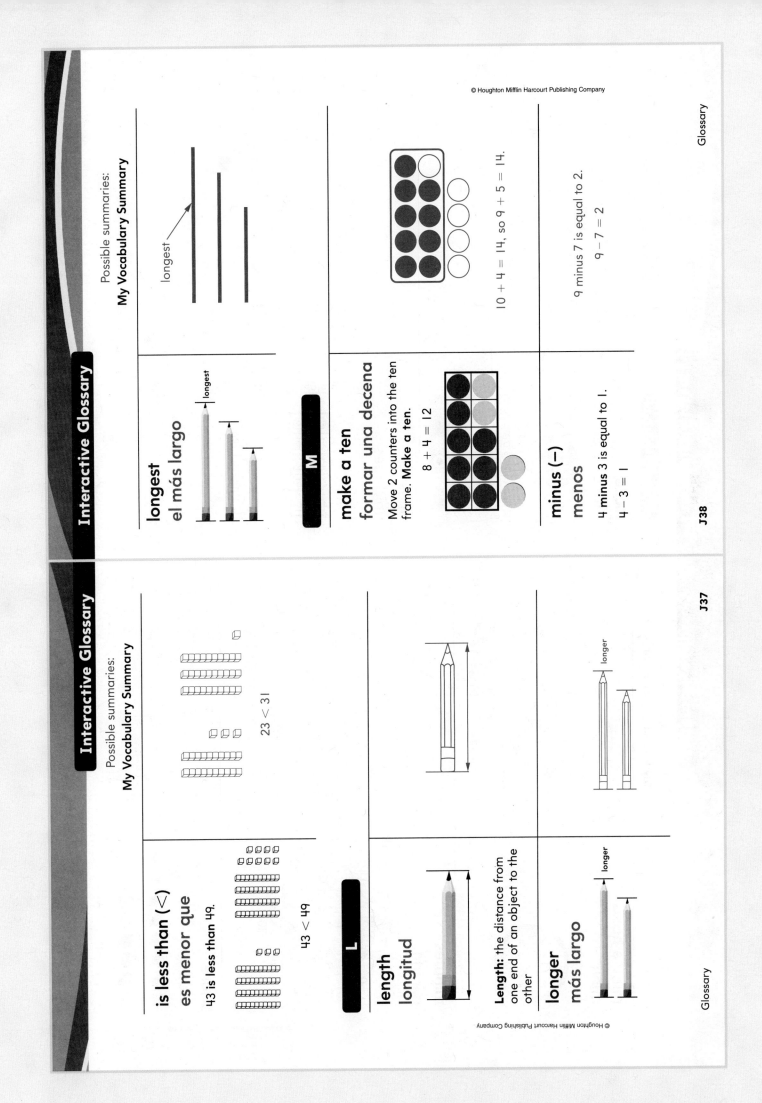

Interactive Glossary

longest
el más largo

longest

Possible summaries:
My Vocabulary Summary

longest

M

make a ten
formar una decena

Move 2 counters into the ten frame. **Make a ten.**

$8 + 4 = 12$

$10 + 4 = 14$, so $9 + 5 = 14$.

minus (−)
menos

4 minus 3 is equal to 1.

$4 − 3 = 1$

9 minus 7 is equal to 2.

$9 − 7 = 2$

Interactive Glossary

is less than (<)
es menor que

43 is less than 49.

$43 < 49$

Possible summaries:
My Vocabulary Summary

$23 < 31$

L

length
longitud

Length: the distance from one end of an object to the other

longer
más largo

longer

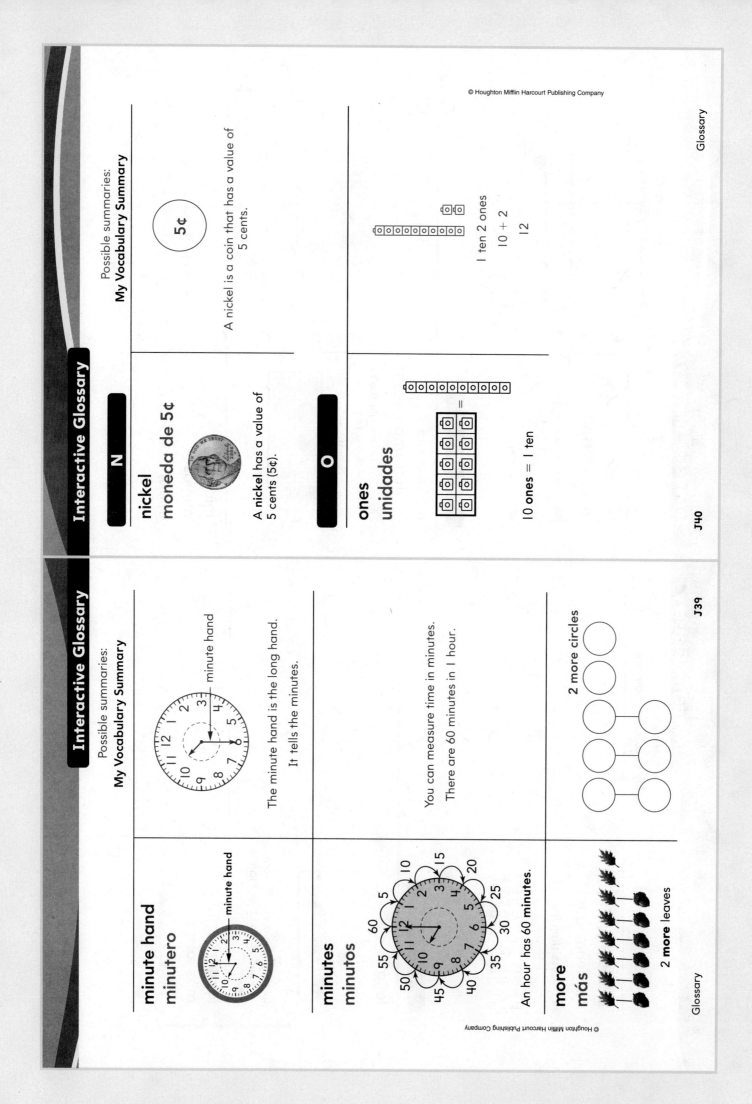

Interactive Glossary

N

nickel
moneda de 5¢

A nickel has a value of 5 cents (5¢).

Possible summaries:
My Vocabulary Summary

5¢

A nickel is a coin that has a value of 5 cents.

O

ones
unidades

10 ones = 1 ten

1 ten 2 ones
10 + 2
12

J40

Interactive Glossary

minute hand
minutero

minute hand

Possible summaries:
My Vocabulary Summary

minute hand

The minute hand is the long hand.

It tells the minutes.

minutes
minutos

An hour has 60 minutes.

You can measure time in minutes.
There are 60 minutes in 1 hour.

more
más

2 more leaves

2 more circles

J39

Interactive Glossary

Q

quarter
moneda de 25¢

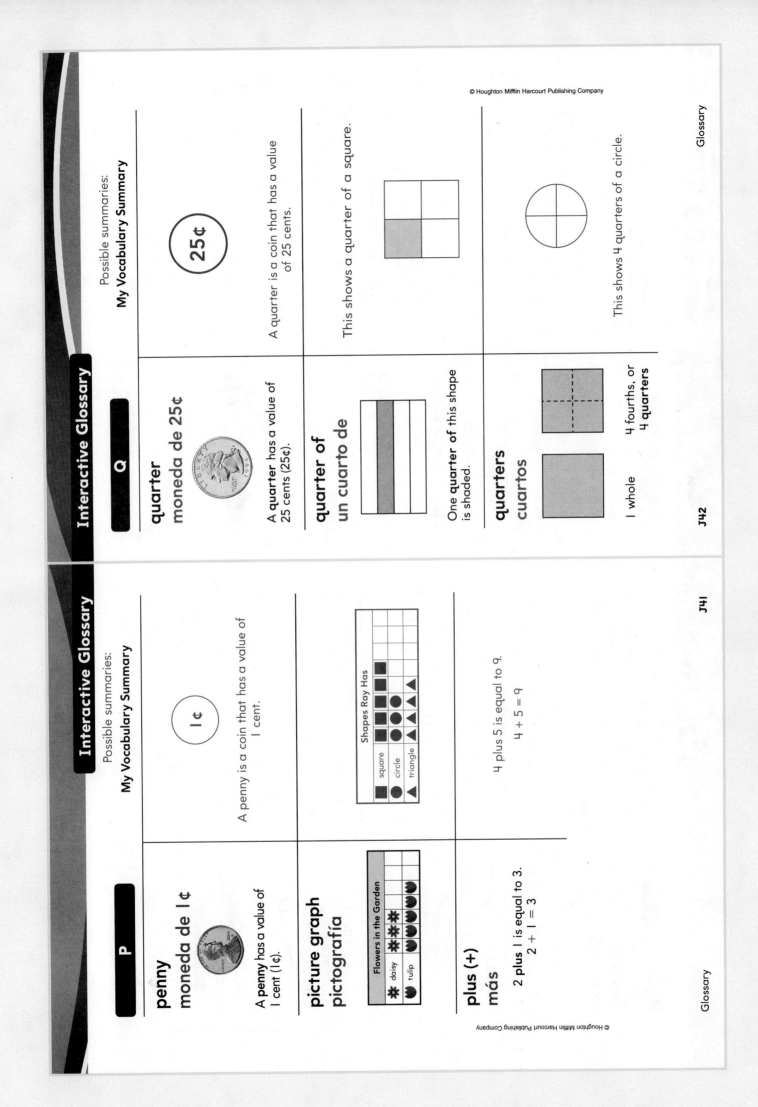

A quarter has a value of 25 cents (25¢).

Possible summaries:
My Vocabulary Summary

25¢

A quarter is a coin that has a value of 25 cents.

quarter of
un cuarto de

One quarter of this shape is shaded.

This shows a quarter of a square.

quarters
cuartos

1 whole

4 fourths, or
4 **quarters**

This shows 4 quarters of a circle.

J42

Interactive Glossary

P

penny
moneda de 1¢

A penny has a value of 1 cent (1¢).

Possible summaries:
My Vocabulary Summary

1¢

A penny is a coin that has a value of 1 cent.

picture graph
pictografía

Flowers in the Garden

| daisy | ❋ | ❋ | | | |
| tulip | ◗ | ◗ | ◗ | ◗ | ◗ |

Shapes Ray Has

square	■	■	■	■	
circle	●	●	●		
triangle	▲	▲	▲	▲	

plus (+)
más

2 plus 1 is equal to 3.
2 + 1 = 3

4 plus 5 is equal to 9.
4 + 5 = 9

J41

Interactive Glossary

S

Possible summaries:
My Vocabulary Summary

shorter
más corto

shortest
el más corto

side
lado

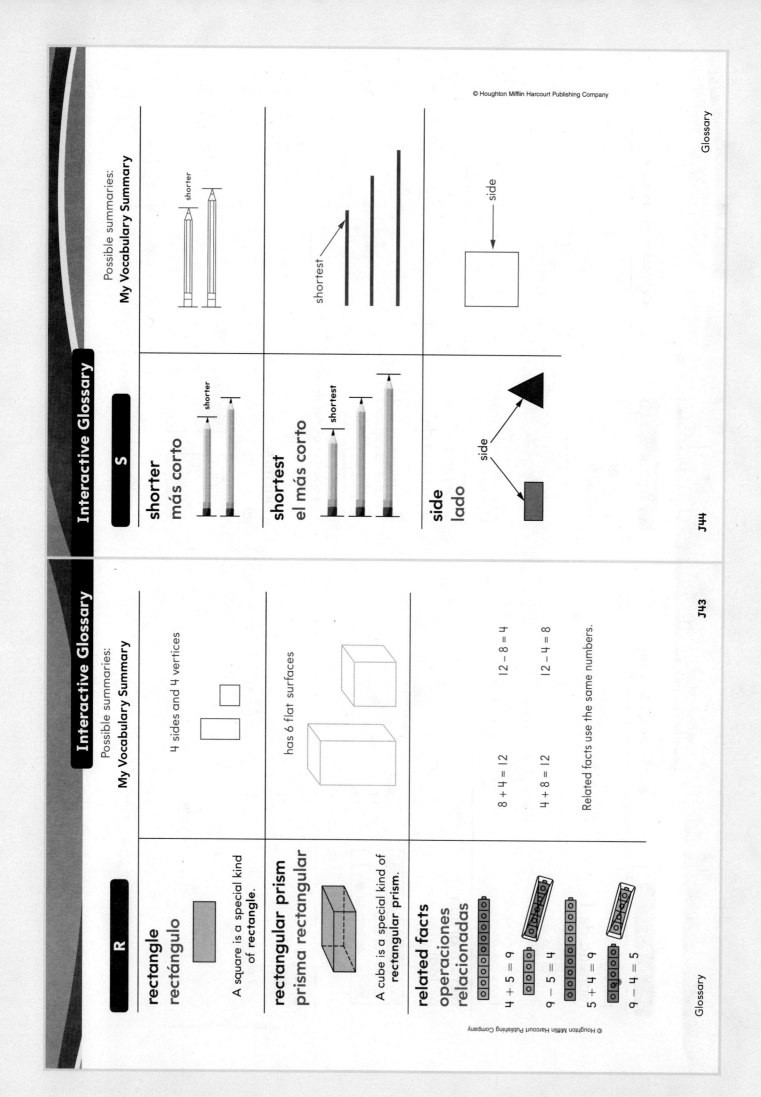

Interactive Glossary

R

Possible summaries:
My Vocabulary Summary

rectangle
rectángulo
A square is a special kind of rectangle.

4 sides and 4 vertices

rectangular prism
prisma rectangular
A cube is a special kind of rectangular prism.

has 6 flat surfaces

related facts
operaciones relacionadas

$4 + 5 = 9$

$9 - 5 = 4$

$5 + 4 = 9$

$9 - 4 = 5$

$8 + 4 = 12$ $12 - 8 = 4$

$4 + 8 = 12$ $12 - 4 = 8$

Related facts use the same numbers.

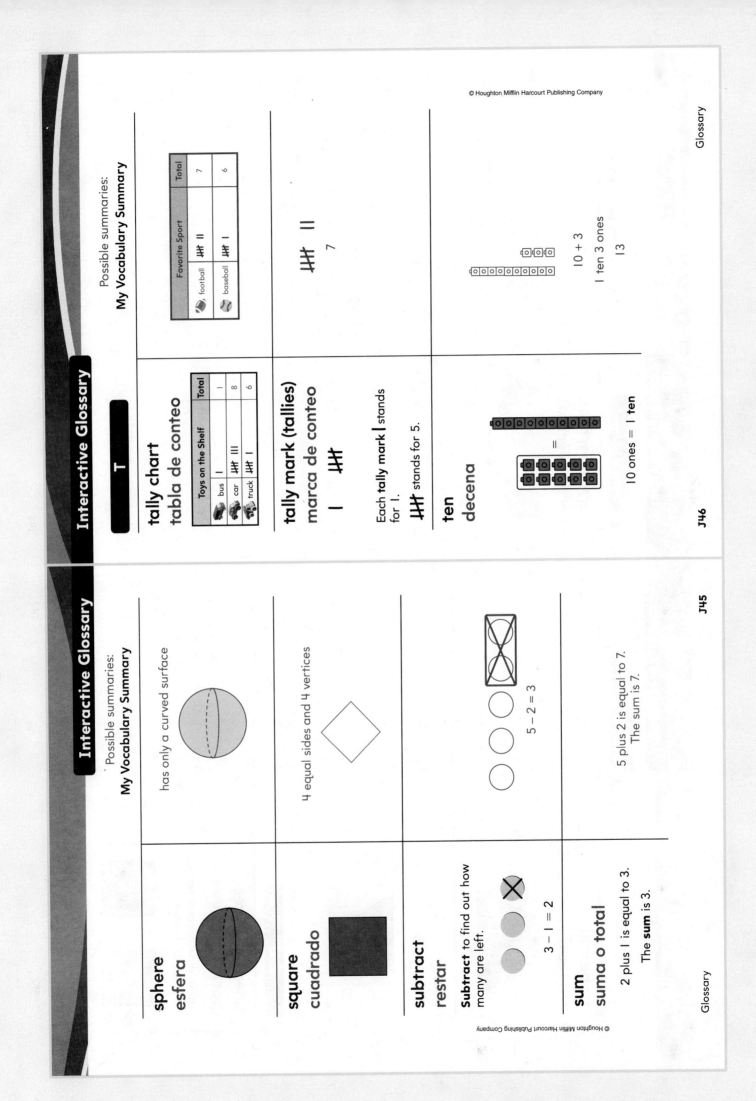

Interactive Glossary

T

tally chart
tabla de conteo

Toys on the Shelf		Total
bus	I	1
car	⊪ III	8
truck	⊪ I	6

tally mark (tallies)
marca de conteo

I   ⊪

Each **tally** mark I stands for I.
⊪ stands for 5.

ten
decena

10 ones = I **ten**

Possible summaries:
My Vocabulary Summary

Favorite Sport		Total
football	⊪ II	7
baseball	⊪ I	6

⊪ = II
7

10 + 3
I ten 3 ones
13

Interactive Glossary

Possible summaries:
My Vocabulary Summary

sphere
esfera

has only a curved surface

square
cuadrado

4 equal sides and 4 vertices

subtract
restar

Subtract to find out how many are left.

5 – 2 = 3

3 – 1 = 2

sum
suma o total

5 plus 2 is equal to 7.
The **sum** is 7.

2 plus I is equal to 3.
The **sum** is 3.

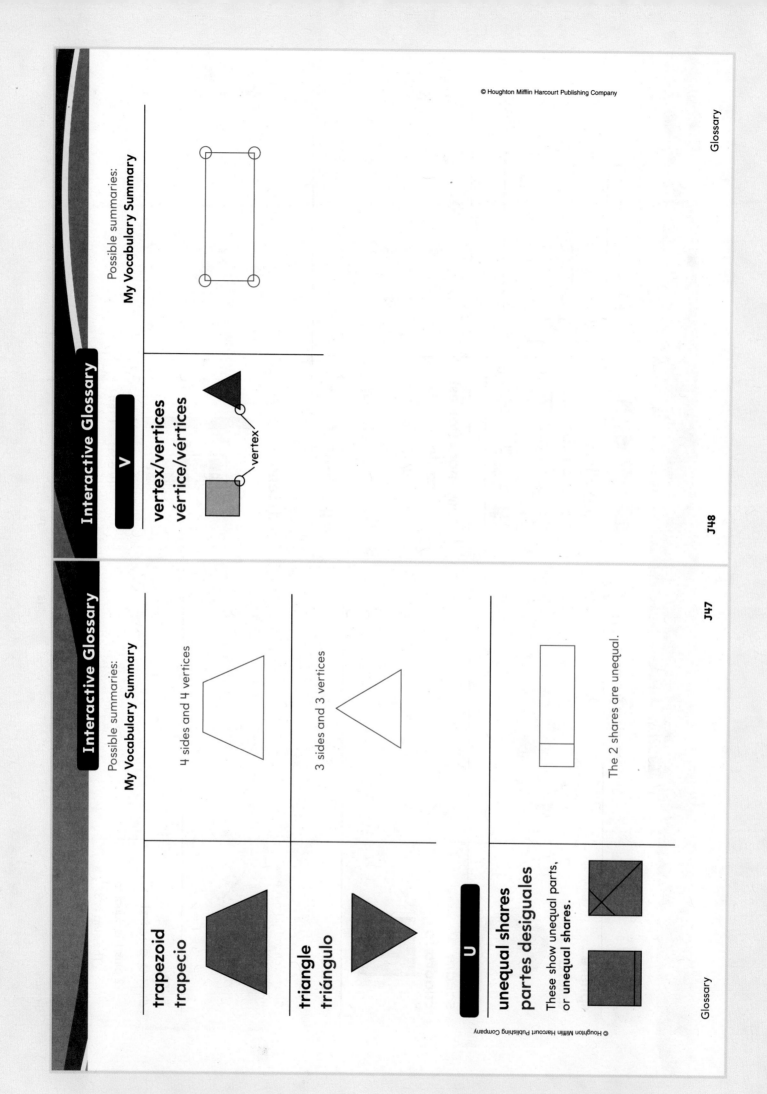

Interactive Glossary

V

vertex/vertices
vértice/vértices

vertex

Possible summaries:
My Vocabulary Summary

Glossary

J48

Interactive Glossary

Possible summaries:
My Vocabulary Summary

trapezoid
trapecio

4 sides and 4 vertices

triangle
triángulo

3 sides and 3 vertices

U

unequal shares
partes desiguales

These show unequal parts,
or unequal shares.

The 2 shares are unequal.

Glossary

J47

Notes & Reflections

Index

A

About the Math. *See under* Professional Learning

addends
  grouping, 85–88, 89–92, 93–96
  order of, 77–80, 81–84
  unknown addend(s)
    Put Together/Take Apart problems with, 173–176, 177–180, 187–192, 193–196, 197–202
    use subtraction to find, 117–120, 121–124, 129–132, 133–136

addition
  add 10 and more, 15–18
  Add To problems
    change unknown, 151–154, 159–164
    result unknown, 147–150, 159–164
    start unknown, 155–158, 159–164
  base ten
    with a hundred chart, 357–360, 361–364, 387–390
    make ten to add, 369–374, 375–378, 403–406
    of tens, 349–352, 357–360
    of tens and ones, 365–368
  Compare problems
    bigger unknown, 211–214, 225–230
    difference unknown, 207–210, 219–224
    smaller unknown, 215–218, 225–230
    strategies for, 231–234
  fact fluency, 103–106, 403–406
  with hundred chart, 357–360, 361–364, 387–390
  by place value, 391–394
  practice, 403–406, 407–410
  properties of
    add three numbers, 85–88, 89–92, 93–96
    order of addends, 77–80, 81–84
  Put Together/Take Apart problems
    addend(s) unknown, 173–176, 177–180, 187–192, 193–196, 197–202
    total unknown, 169–172, 181–186, 193–196, 197–202
  represent, 5–8
  strategies
    for adding 3 numbers, 89–92, 93–96
    count on, 9–14, 33–38, 232
    doubles facts, 25–28, 29–32, 33–38
    known sums, 29–32, 33–38
    make 10, 19–24, 33–38, 231, 369–374, 375–378, 403–406
    for two-digit numbers, 399–402
  subtraction, relationship with
    add to subtract strategy, 57–60, 67–72, 111–116, 404
    check with addition, 125–128
    related facts (*see* related facts)
  of two-digit numbers
    on hundred chart, 357–360, 361–364, 387–390
    make 10, 369–374, 375–378
    by place value, 391–394
    strategies, 399–402

addition facts
  doubles, 25–28, 29–32, 33–38
  fact fluency, 103–106, 403–406

  related facts
    add to check subtraction, 125–128
    add to subtract, 57–60, 67–72, 111–116, 404
    identify, 121–124
    represent, 117–120
    unknown addends and, 129–132, 133–136

Add To problems
  change unknown, 151–154, 159–164
  result unknown, 147–150, 159–164
  start unknown, 155–158, 159–164

algebra
  addition
    Add To problems, 147–150, 151–154, 155–158, 159–164
    Compare problems, 207–210, 211–214, 215–218, 219–224, 225–230, 231–234
    grouping, 85–88, 89–92, 93–96
    make 10 to add, 19–24, 33–38, 231, 369–374, 375–378, 403
    order of addends, 77–80, 81–84
    Put Together/Take Apart problems, 169–172, 173–176, 177–180, 181–186, 187–192, 193–196, 197–202
    unknown addend(s), 117–120, 129–132, 133–136, 173–176, 177–180, 187–192, 193–196, 197–202
  properties of addition
    add three numbers, 85–88, 89–92, 93–96
    order of addends, 77–80, 81–84
  subtraction
    add to subtract, 57–60, 67–72, 111–116, 404
    Compare problems, 207–210, 215–218, 219–224, 225–230, 231–234
    Put Together/Take Apart problems, 169–172, 173–176, 177–180, 187–192, 197–202
    Take From problems, 147–150, 151–154, 155–158, 159–164
    use 10 to subtract, 61–66, 67–72

anchor chart, every module includes a completed anchor chart. *8B, 46B, 80B, 116B, 150B, 172B, 210B, 248B, 282B, 298B, 328B, 352B, 390B, 422B, 438B, 462B, 484B, 504B*
  Anchor charts are also available in the *Teacher Edition: Planning and Pacing Guide PG93–PG110*

Are You Ready?, appears in every module. 4, 42, 76, 110, 146, 168, 206, 244, 278, 294, 324, 348, 386, 416, 434, 458, 480, 500

assessment
  Are You Ready?, appears in every module. 4, 42, 76, 110, 146, 168, 206, 244, 278, 294, 324, 348, 386, 416, 434, 458, 480, 500
  Check Understanding, appears in every lesson. *See, for example,* 7, 12, 17, 22, 27, 31, 35, 171, 175, 179, 184, 190, 194, 199, 461, 465, 469, 473
  diagnostic assessment
    Are You Ready? (*see* Are You Ready?)
  formative assessment
    Check Understanding (*see* Check Understanding)
  Module Review, every module includes a Module Review with a possible scoring guide for all items. *39–40,*

  73–74, 107–108, 141–142, 165–166, 203–204, 241–242, 273–274, 291–292, 321–322, 343–344, 383–384, 411–412, 431–432, 455–456, 475–476, 497–498, 517–518
  Module Test, every module includes a Module Test with an alternate version. *40A, 74A, 108A, 142A, 166A, 204A, 242A, 274A, 292A, 322A, 344A, 384A, 412A, 432A, 456A, 476A, 498A, 518A*
  summative assessment
    Module Review (*see* Module Review)
    Module Test (*see* Module Test)

B

bar graphs, 261–264, 265–268, 269–272

bar models
  for Compare problems, 220–224, 226–230
  for Put Together/Take Apart problems, 181–186, 187–192, 193–196, 197–202

base ten
  addition
    with a hundred chart, 357–360, 361–364, 387–390
    make 10 to add, 369–374, 375–378
    of tens, 349–352, 357–360
    of tens and ones, 365–368
  mental math, 379–382
  subtraction of tens, 353–356, 357–360, 387–390

C

Check Understanding, appears in every lesson. *See, for example,* 7, 12, 17, 22, 27, 31, 35, 171, 175, 179, 184, 190, 194, 199, 460, 465, 469, 473

circle, 437, 442, 443, 461, 465, 468–470, 472, 473

Collect and Display. *See under* language routines

combine shapes
  three-dimensional, 423–426, 427–430
  two-dimensional, 443–446, 447–450, 451–454, 459–462

compare
  by length, 481–484, 485–488
  numbers, 325–328, 329–332, 333–336, 337–342

Compare and Connect. *See under* language routines

Compare problems
  bigger unknown, 211–214, 225–230
  difference unknown, 207–210, 219–224
  smaller unknown, 215–218, 225–230
  strategies for, 231–234

composite shapes
  three-dimensional, 423–426, 427–430
  two-dimensional, 443–446, 447–450, 451–454, 459–462

cone, 419

count back, to subtract, 47–52, 67–72

count on
  to add, 9–14, 33–38, 232
  to subtract, 53–56, 67–72

count to 120, 295–298

TE Book 1 . . . . 1–40A	TE Book 6 . . . . 167A–204A	TE Book 11 . . . . 345–384A	*Teacher Edition: Planning and Pacing Guide* PG1–PG128
TE Book 2 . . . . 41A–74A	TE Book 7 . . . . 205A–242A	TE Book 12 . . . . 385A–412A	
TE Book 3 . . . . 75A–108A	TE Book 8 . . . . 243A–274A	TE Book 13 . . . . 413–456A	Teacher Edition references are in italics;
TE Book 4 . . . . 109A–142A	TE Book 9 . . . . 275–322A	TE Book 14 . . . . 457A–476A	*Teacher Edition: Planning and Pacing Guide* references begin with PG.
TE Book 5 . . . . 143–166A	TE Book 10 . . . . 323A–344A	TE Book 15 . . . . 477–518A	

Critique, Correct, and Clarify. *See under* language
routines

cube, 418

curved surface, 419

cylinder, 419

D

data analysis
bar graphs, 261–264, 265–268, 269–272
picture graphs, 245–248, 249–252
problem solving with, 269–272
tally charts, 253–256, 257–260, 268, 269, 272

data checkpoint, every module includes an autoscored
Are You Ready? diagnostic assessment and a Module
Test summative assessment. Every lesson includes an
autoscored Check Understanding formative assessment.
When you assign autoscored assignments on Ed: Your
Friend in Learning, you will have immediate access to data
and recommendations for differentiation.
Are You Ready?, appears in every module. *4, 42, 76, 110,
146, 168, 206, 244, 278, 294, 324, 348, 386, 416, 434,
458, 480, 500*
Check Understanding, appears in every lesson. *See, for
example, 7, 12, 17, 22, 27, 31, 35, 171, 175, 179, 184,
190, 194, 199, 461, 465, 469, 473*
Module Test, *40A, 74A, 108A, 142A, 166A, 204A, 242A,
274A, 292A, 322A, 344A, 384A, 412A, 432A, 456A, 476A,
498A, 518A*

data-driven instruction, every module includes
data charts to help you drive instruction to support
students for the Are You Ready? and Module Review
assessments. Every lesson includes differentiation support
following the Check Understanding assessment to support
students. *Teacher Edition: Planning and Pacing Guide
PG24–PG31*

decompose numbers, 307–312

developing math language, *3C, 41C, 75C, 109C,
145C, 167C, 205C, 243C, 277C, 293C, 323C, 347C, 385C,
415C, 433C, 457C, 479C, 499C*

diagnostic assessment
Are You Ready? (*see* Are You Ready?)

difference, 44

differentiated instruction, every lesson includes
leveled activities for pulled small groups and leveled print
and digital activities for Math Centers. Some examples are
*5C, 9C, 15C, 19C, 25C, 29C, 33C, 43C, 47C, 53C, 57C, 61C,
67C, 77C, 81C, 85C, 89C, 93C*

doubles, 25–28, 29–32, 33–38

E

equality
determine, 97–102
equal shares, 463–466, 467–470, 471–474
is equal to (=), 6, 333–336

equation, 6, 350

Exit Ticket, every lesson provides a projectable Exit Ticket.
Some examples are *8, 14, 18, 24, 28, 32, 38, 46, 52, 56, 60,
66, 72, 80, 84, 88, 92, 96, 102, 106, 116*

F

fact fluency, 103–106, 137–140, 403–406

figures. *See* three-dimensional shapes; two-dimensional
shapes

flat surfaces, 418, 420

formative assessment
Check Understanding (*see* Check Understanding)

fourths and fourth of, 471–474

G

geometry. *See* three-dimensional shapes; two-
dimensional shapes

Glossary. *See More Practice and Homework Journal* for the
student Interactive Glossary. *See Teacher Edition: Planning
and Pacing Guide* PG112–PG122 for the teacher Interactive
Glossary.

graphs
bar graphs, 261–264, 265–268, 269–272
picture graphs, 245–248, 249–252

greater than
is greater than (>), 325–328, 333–336, 337–342

grouping
addends, 85–88, 89–92, 93–96

H

half hour, 505–508, 509–512, 513–516

halves and half of, 467–470

hexagon, 440

hour, 501–504, 509–512, 513–516

hour hand, 502

hundred chart, 357–360, 361–364, 387–390

I

I Can scale, every lesson provides a scale to track progress
on learning goals. Some examples are *8, 14, 18, 24, 28,
32, 38, 46, 52, 56, 60, 66, 72, 80, 84, 88, 92, 96, 102,
106, 116*

indirect measurement, 485–488

Interactive Glossary. *See* Glossary

is equal to (=), 6, 333–336

is greater than (>), 325–328, 333–336, 337–342

is less than (<), 329–332, 333–336, 337–342

J

journal, every lesson provides prompts for journals. Some
examples are *8, 14, 18, 24, 28, 32, 38, 46, 52, 56, 60, 66,
72, 80, 84, 88, 92, 96, 102, 106, 116*

L

language routines
Collect and Display, some examples are *8B, 46B, 80B, 116B,
150B, 172B, 210B, 248B, 282B, 298B*
Compare and Connect, some examples are *5, 6, 9, 10,
15, 19, 20, 25, 26, 29, 43, 44, 47, 48, 53, 57, 61, 77,
78, 81*
Critique, Correct, and Clarify, some examples are *36, 56,
101, 135, 158, 164, 191, 201, 214, 218, 233, 240*
Stronger and Clearer Each Time, some examples are *15, 29,
49, 54, 58, 68, 82, 90, 94,122*
Three Reads, some examples are *5, 9, 15, 25, 29, 43, 47,
53, 57, 77, 81, 85, 111, 117, 121, 125, 129, 147, 155,
173, 177*

Learning Mindset, appears in all unit openers and in
some lessons.
In lessons, some examples are *8, 14, 18, 24, 28, 32, 46, 52,
56, 60, 66, 80, 84, 88, 92, 116, 120, 124, 128, 132, 150,
154, 158, 172, 176, 180, 186, 192, 210, 214*
In unit openers, *2, 144, 276, 346, 414, 478*

length
indirect measurement of, 485–488
nonstandard measurement of, 492–496
order by, 481–484

less than
is less than (<), 329–332, 333–336, 337–342

Leveled Questions, every lesson includes a chart
with leveled questions for Depth of Knowledge 1, 2, and
3 and diagnostic support of what students may know or
understand. Some examples are *6, 10, 16, 20, 26, 30, 33,
44, 48, 54, 58, 62, 67, 78, 82, 86, 90, 93*

longest, 482–484

M

make 10
to add, 19–24, 33–38, 231, 369–374, 375–378, 403
to subtract, 61–66, 67–72

Make Connections. *See under* Warm-Up Options

manipulatives and materials
base-ten blocks, 300, 303–304, 308–309, 313–314,
317–318, 325–327, 329–331, 333, 335, 349–351,
353–355, 357, 361, 365–366, 369–370, 375, 386,
391–392, 395–396
clock, 506, 509

Index

manipulatives and materials (continued)
  connecting cubes, 5–7, 9–11, 15–16, 26–28, 29–32, 43–45, 47–48, 53–54, 57–60, 61, 77–79, 81–82, 85–87, 89, 111–112, 117–120, 121–122, 125–126, 129–130, 147–149, 151–152, 155–156, 169–170, 173, 177–179, 181–182, 187, 219–221, 225–227, 245, 253, 257, 261, 265, 279–281, 283–285, 287–288, 295, 299–300, 303–304, 307–309, 349, 353, 357
  counting chart, 313–314, 317
  hundred chart, 357–360, 361–362, 387–390
  number cube, 61, 147, 169, 187, 295, 349
  pattern blocks, 440, 441, 443, 444–446, 448–450
  place-value chart, 299, 325–327, 330–331, 392–393, 396
  plane shapes, 249, 436–437, 441, 444–446, 449
  square tiles, 78–79, 81, 85, 89, 489
  three-dimensional shapes, 417–419, 423–425, 427–430, 439
  two-color counters, 5–7, 9–11, 15–18, 19–24, 26, 29–30, 43–45, 47–48, 53–54, 57–60, 61–64, 67, 69–70, 77–79, 81–82, 85, 87, 89, 111–112, 117–118, 121–122, 125–126, 129–130, 147–149, 151–152, 155–156, 169–171, 173–175, 177–179, 181, 187, 207–208, 211–212, 215–216, 219, 225, 235–238, 253, 280–281, 283–285

Manipulatives and Tools, *See Teacher Edition: Planning and Pacing Guide PG79–PG81*

Mathematical Practices and Processes
  1. *make sense of problems and persevere in solving them,* occurs throughout. Some examples are 8, 156, 207, 325, 410
  2. *reason abstractly and quantitatively,* in some lessons. Some examples are 72, 80, 290, 381, 390
  3. *construct viable arguments and critique the reasoning of others,* in some lessons. Some examples are 56, 101, 311, 332, 442
  4. *model with mathematics,* in some lessons. Some examples are 52, 70, 95, 150, 352
  5. *use appropriate tools strategically,* in some lessons. Some examples are 18, 51, 65, 302, 364
  6. *attend to precision,* in some lessons. Some examples are 268, 298, 394, 446
  7. *look for and make use of structure,* in some lessons. Some examples are 84, 92, 105, 282, 442
  8. *look for and express regularity in repeated reasoning,* in some lessons. Some examples are 195, 233, 239, 438, 508

Mathematical Progressions, each TE module and lesson includes a Mathematical Progression for current development, prior learning, and future connections.
  In lessons, some examples are *5A, 9A, 15A, 19A, 25A, 29A, 33A, 43A, 47A, 53A, 57A, 61A, 67A, 77A, 81A, 85A, 89A, 93A*
  In modules, *3B, 41B, 75B, 109B, 145B, 167B, 205B, 243B, 277B, 293B, 323B, 347B, 385B, 415B, 433B, 457B, 479B, 499B*

Math on the Spot videos, some lessons feature a Math on the Spot video problem. Some examples are *14A, 18A, 32A, 52A, 80A, 84A, 88A, 96A, 102A, 106A, 116A, 120A, 124A, 224A, 286A, 302A, 328A, 332A*

  See also student and parent resources on Ed: Your Friend in Learning

Math Routine. *See under* Warm-Up Options

Math Teaching Practices
  1. *establish mathematics goals to focus learning,* occurs throughout. Some examples are *41B, 43A, 457B, 459A*
  2. *implement tasks that promote reasoning and problem solving,* occurs throughout. Some examples are *3B, 53D, 54, 75B, 129A*
  3. *use and connect mathematical representations,* occurs throughout. Some examples are *145B, 147D, 148, 205B, 207D, 208*
  4. *facilitate meaningful mathematical discourse,* occurs throughout. Some examples are *54, 57, 58, 61, 169B, 347B*
  5. *pose purposeful questions,* occurs throughout. Some examples are *109B, 143, 145C, 147, 167B, 167C, 169*
  6. *build procedural fluency from conceptual understanding,* occurs throughout. Some examples are *145B, 347B*
  7. *support productive struggle in learning mathematics,* occurs throughout. Some examples are *3B, 12, 17, 22, 27, 29, 31, 35, 43B, 49, 55*
  8. *elicit and use evidence of student thinking,* occurs throughout. Some examples are *41B, 43, 47, 53, 109B, 111, 117, 121, 125*

measure
  length
    indirect measurement of, 485–488
    nonstandard measurement of, 493–496
    order by, 481–484
  time
    to the half hour, 505–508, 509–512, 513–516
    to the hour, 501–504, 505–506, 509–512, 513–516

minus (−), 44. *See also* subtraction

minute hand, 510

Module Opening Task, 3, 41, 75, 109, 145, 167, 205, 243, 277, 293, 323, 347, 385, 401, 415, 433, 456, 479, 499

module planning, 3A, 41A, 75A, 109A, 145A, 167A, 205A, 243A, 277A, 293A, 323A, 347A, 385A, 401A, 415A, 433A, 457A, 479A, 499A

Module Review, every module includes a Module Review with a possible scoring guide for all items. *39–40, 73–74, 107–108, 141–142, 165–166, 203–204, 241–242, 273–274, 291–292, 321–322, 343–344, 383–384, 411–412, 431–432, 455–456, 475–476, 497–498, 517–518*

Module Test, every module includes a Module Test with an alternate version. *40A, 74A, 108A, 142A, 166A, 204A, 242A, 274A, 292A, 322A, 344A, 384A, 412A, 432A, 456A, 476A, 498A, 518A*

numbers. *See also* place value; three-digit numbers; two-digit numbers

compare
  is equal to, 333–336
  is greater than, 325–328, 333–336, 337–342
  is less than, 329–332, 333–336, 337–342
  to solve problems, 337–342
count to 120, 295–298
decompose in different ways, 307–312
read and write to 120, 313–316, 317–320
represent, 277, 279–282, 283–286, 287–290, 299–302, 303–306, 313–316, 317–320

O

ones
  addition of tens and, 365–368
  representations of, 279–282, 283–286, 299–302, 303–306, 307–312
  of teen numbers, 279–282, 283–286
order
  of addends, 77–80, 81–84
  by length, 481–484

P

pacing, *Teacher Edition: Planning and Pacing Guide PG46–PG60*

picture graphs, 245–248, 249–252

place value. *See also* base ten
  add by, 391–394
  compare by, 325–328, 329–332, 333–336, 337–342
  decompose in different ways, 307–312
  ones representations, 279–282, 283–286, 299–302, 303–306, 307–312
  subtract by, 395–398
  of teen numbers, 279–282, 283–286
  tens, groups of, 287–290
  tens representations, 287–290, 299–302, 303–306, 307–312

plane figures. *See* two-dimensional shapes

plus (+), 6. *See also* addition

prerequisite skills. *See also* Are You Ready?
  for addition, 4, 76, 110, 146, 168, 348, 386
  for Compare problems, 206
  for comparisons of numbers, 324
  for counting, 294, 324
  for data, 244
  for fractions, 468
  for length measurement, 480
  for number representation, 294
  for place value, 278
  for properties of operations, 76
  for subtraction, 42, 110, 146, 168, 348, 386
  for three-dimensional shapes, 416
  for time measurement, 500
  for two-dimensional shapes, 434

Prerequisite Skills Activity. *See under* Warm-Up Options

TE Book 1 . . . . *1–40A*	TE Book 6 . . . . *167A–204A*	TE Book 11 . . . . *345–384A*
TE Book 2 . . . . *41A–74A*	TE Book 7 . . . . *205A–242A*	TE Book 12 . . . . *385A–412A*
TE Book 3 . . . . *75A–108A*	TE Book 8 . . . . *243A–274A*	TE Book 13 . . . . *413–456A*
TE Book 4 . . . . *109A–142A*	TE Book 9 . . . . *275–322A*	TE Book 14 . . . . *457A–476A*
TE Book 5 . . . . *143–166A*	TE Book 10 . . . . *323A–344A*	TE Book 15 . . . . *477–518A*

Teacher Edition: Planning and Pacing Guide PG1–PG128

Teacher Edition references are in italics;
Teacher Edition: Planning and Pacing Guide references begin with PG.

problem situations
  Add To, 147–150, 151–154, 155–158, 159–164
  Compare, 207–210, 211–214, 215–218, 219–224, 225–230, 231–234, 235–240
  Put Together, 169–172, 173–176, 177–180, 181–186, 187–192, 193–196, 197–202
  Take Apart, 177–180, 187–192, 197–202
  Take From, 147–150, 151–154, 155–158, 159–164

Problem Types, PG69–PG74

Professional Learning
  About the Math, some examples are *47A, 57A, 111A, 117A, 129A, 147A, 169A, 207A, 245A, 279A, 287A*
  Using Mathematical Practices and Processes, some examples are *43A, 111A, 125A, 133A, 151A, 155A, 173A, 181A, 187A, 211A, 215A, 231A*
  Visualizing the Math, some examples are *67A, 89A, 117A, 121A, 129A, 197A, 219A, 257A*

properties of addition
  add three numbers, 85–88, 89–92, 93–96
  order of addends, 77–80, 81–84

Put It in Writing. *See* journal

Put Together/Take Apart problems
  addend(s) unknown, 173–176, 177–180, 187–192, 193–196, 197–202
  total unknown, 169–172, 181–186, 193–196, 197–202

Q

quarters (fourths), 471–474

R

rectangle
  attributes of, 436–438
  composite shapes, 443–446, 447–450, 451–454
  describe and draw, 439–442
  equal shares of, 463–466, 467–470, 471–474

rectangular prism, 418, 420–421, 423–426, 427–430

related facts
  add to check subtraction, 125–128
  add to subtract, 57–60, 67–72, 111–116
  identify, 121–124
  represent, 117–120
    unknown addends and, 129–132, 133–136

represent
  addend(s) unknown problems, 173–175, 177–179, 187
  addition
    to check subtraction, 125–128
    count on strategy, 9–14
    doubles strategy, 25–28
    equation, 5–8

    known sums strategy, 29–32
    make 10 strategy, 19–24, 369–374, 375–378
    by place value, 391–392
    properties of, 77–80, 81–82, 85–88, 89
    of two-digit numbers, 349–352, 357–360, 361–364, 365–366, 387–390
  bigger unknown problems, 211–214, 225–230
  change unknown problems, 151–154
  composite shapes, 447–449, 451–454, 458
  data organization, 245, 249–252, 253, 257–260, 265–268, 269–272
  difference unknown problems, 207–210, 219–224
  equal shares, 463, 467–469, 471–473
  groups of ten, 287–290
    length, 481–483, 485, 489–490
  number comparisons, 325–328, 329–331, 333
  numbers, 277, 279–282, 283–286, 287–290, 299–302, 303–306, 307–312, 313–316, 317–320
  place value, 277, 279–282, 283–286, 287–290, 299–302, 303–306, 307–309
  plane shapes, 441, 444–446
  related facts, 111–112, 117–120, 121–122, 129–130
  result unknown problems, 147–150
  smaller unknown problems, 215–218, 225–226
  start unknown problems, 155–156
  subtraction
    add to subtract, 57–60
    count back, 47–52
    count on to subtract, 53–55
    equation, 43–46
    make 10, 61–66
    by place value, 395–398
    of tens, 353–356, 357–360
    of two-digit numbers, 387–390
  teen numbers, 279–282, 283–286
  three-dimensional shapes, 417–420, 423–425, 427–429
  time, 501–504, 505–508, 509–512, 513–516
  total unknown problems, 169–171, 181–182
  two-dimensional shapes, 435–437, 439–441, 443

Response to Intervention/Multi-Tiered System of Support (RtI/MTSS), options can be found at point of use. Some examples are *4, 5C, 9C, 15C, 19C, 25C, 39, 40, 42, 43C, 47C, 53C, 57C, 73, 74, 76, 77C, 81C, 85C, 89C, 107, 108, 110, 111C, 117C, 125C, 129C, 141, 142, 146, 168*
See also Teacher Edition: Planning and Pacing Guide PG42

S

shapes. *See* three-dimensional shapes; two-dimensional shapes

Sharpen Skills. *See under* Warm-Up Options

shortest, 482

sides, of two-dimensional shapes, 436–437, 440

solid figures. *See* three-dimensional shapes

sort
  to represent data, 243, 245, 253
  three-dimensional shapes, 417–420
  two-dimensional shapes, 435–438

Spark Your Learning. *See under* student samples

sphere, 415, 416, 419, 420, 422

square, 436–437, 441, 445, 452

standards correlations, *Teacher Edition: Planning and Pacing Guide* PG63–PG68

STEM Task, 1, 143, 275, 345, 413, 477

Step It Out. *See under* student samples

Stronger and Clearer Each Time. *See under* language routines

student samples
  Spark Your Learning, *5D, 9D, 15D, 19D, 25D, 29D, 33D, 43D, 47D, 53D, 57D, 61D, 67D, 77D, 81D, 85D, 89D, 97D, 111D, 117D, 121D, 125D, 129D, 147D, 151D, 155D, 159D, 169D, 173D, 177D, 181D, 187D, 197D, 207D, 211D, 215D, 219D, 225D, 235D, 245D, 249D, 253D, 257D, 261D, 265D, 279D, 283D, 287D, 295D, 299D, 303D, 307D, 313D, 317D, 325D, 329D, 333D, 337D, 349D, 353D, 357D, 361D, 365D, 369D, 375D, 387D, 391D, 395D, 417D, 423D, 427D, 435D, 439D, 443D, 447D, 451D, 459D, 463D, 467D, 471D, 481D, 485D, 489D, 493D, 501D, 505D, 509D*
  Step It Out, *33D, 67D, 93D, 97D, 103D, 133D, 137D, 159D, 193D, 197D, 269D, 399D, 403D, 407D*

subtraction
  addition relationship with
    add to subtract strategy, 57–60, 67–72, 111–116
    check with addition, 125–128
    find an unknown addend, 129–132
    related facts (*see* related facts)
  Compare problems
    difference unknown, 207–210, 219–224
    smaller unknown, 215–218, 225–230
    strategies for, 231–234
  fact fluency, 137–140, 403–406
  with hundred chart, 387–390
  by place value, 395–398
  practice, 403–406, 407–410
  Put Together/Take Apart problems, 177–180, 187–192, 197–202
  represent, 43–46
  strategies
    add to subtract, 57–60, 67–72, 111–116
    count back to subtract, 47–52, 67–72
    count on to subtract, 53–56, 67–72
  Take From problems
    change unknown, 151–154, 159–164
    result unknown, 147–150, 159–164
    start unknown, 155–158, 159–164
    for two-digit numbers, 399–400

Index

subtraction *(continued)*
  of tens, 353–356, 357–360
  of two-digit numbers
    on hundred chart, 387–390
    by place value, 395–398
    strategies, 399–402
    by tens, 353–356, 357–360, 375–378
sum. *See* addition
summative assessment
  Module Review (*see* Module Review)
  Module Test (*see* Module Test)
symbols
  to compare, 333–336, 340, 342
  is equal to (=), 6, 333–336
  is greater than (>), 333–336
  is less than (<), 333–336
  minus (−), 44
  plus (+), 6

T

Table of Measures. *See More Practice and Homework Journal*
Tabletop Flipcharts Mini-Lesson, every lesson includes a Tabletop Flipchart Mini-Lesson for teachers to use with a small, pulled group of students who are almost there. Some examples are *5C, 9C, 15C, 19C, 25C, 29C, 33C, 43C, 47C, 53C, 57C, 61C, 67C, 77C, 81C, 85C, 89C, 93C*
Take From problems
  change unknown, 151–154, 159–164
  result unknown, 147–150, 159–164
  start unknown, 155–158, 159–164
tally charts, 253–256, 257–260, 268, 269, 272
tally marks (tallies), 254
Teacher to Teacher, *3B, 41B, 75B, 109B, 145B, 167B, 205B, 243B, 277B, 293B, 323B, 347B, 385B, 401B, 415B, 433B, 456B, 479B, 499B*
Teaching for Depth, *3B, 41B, 75B, 109B, 145B, 167B, 205B, 243B, 277B, 293B, 323B, 347B, 385B, 401B, 415B, 433B, 457B, 479B, 499B*
technology and digital resources. *See* Ed: Your Friend in Learning for interactive instruction, interactive practice, and videos
teen numbers, 279–282, 283–286
tens
  addition of, 349–352, 357–360, 361–364, 365–368
  groups of, 287–290
  representations of, 287–290, 299–302, 303–306, 307–312
  subtraction of, 353–356, 357–360
  of teen numbers, 279–282, 283–286
three-digit numbers, 313–316, 317–320
three-dimensional shapes
  attributes of, 417–420
  composite, 423–426, 427–430

Three Reads. *See under* language routines
time
  to the half hour, 505–508, 509–512, 513–516
  to the hour, 501–504, 505–506, 509–512, 513–516
trapezoid, 440, 441, 444, 450, 453, 455
triangle, 436–438, 446, 449, 453
two-digit numbers
  addition
    on hundred chart, 357–360, 361–364, 387–390
    make 10 to add, 369–374, 375–378
    by place value, 391–394
    practice, 407–410
    strategies, 399–402
    of tens, 349–352, 357–360
    represent, 277–278, 279–282, 283–286, 287–290, 299–302, 303–306, 307–312
  subtraction
    on hundred chart, 357–360, 387–390
    by place value, 395–398
    strategies, 399–402
    of tens, 353–356, 357–360
two-dimensional shapes
  attributes of, 436–438, 439–442
  composite, 443–446, 447–450, 451–454, 459–462
  equal shares of, 463–466, 467–470, 471–474

U

unequal shares, 463–466
Unit Opener, 1–2, 143–144, 275–276, 345–346, 413–414, 477–478
Unit Performance Task, PG83–PG88
unknown
  addend(s)
    Put Together/Take Apart problems with, 173–176, 177–180, 187–192, 193–196, 197–202
    use subtraction to find, 129–132, 133–136
  Add To problems
    change unknown, 151–154, 159–164
    result unknown, 147–150, 159–164
    start unknown, 155–158, 159–164
  Compare problems
    bigger unknown, 211–214, 225–230
    difference unknown, 207–210, 219–224
    smaller unknown, 215–218, 225–230
    strategies for, 231–234
  Put Together/Take Apart problems
    addend(s) unknown, 173–176, 177–180, 187–192, 193–196, 197–202
    total unknown, 169–172, 181–186, 193–196, 197–202
  Take From problems
    change unknown, 151–154, 159–164
    result unknown, 147–150, 159–164
    start unknown, 155–158, 159–164

Unpacking Math Standards, *5A, 9A, 15A, 47A, 57A, 77A, 85A, 97A, 111A, 117A, 129A, 147A, 169A, 207A, 245A, 279A, 287A, 295A, 299A, 313A, 317A, 325A, 333A, 349A, 353A, 379A, 387A, 391A, 417A, 423A, 435A, 443A, 459A, 463A, 481A, 485A, 489A, 501A*
use known sums to add, 29–32, 33–38, 231
Using Mathematical Practices and Processes. *See under* Professional Learning

V

vertex, 436
Visualizing the Math. *See under* Professional Learning

W
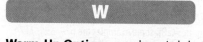

Warm-Up Options, every lesson includes the warm-up options Make Connections, Math Routines, Prerequisite Skills Activity, and Sharpen Skills. Some examples are *5B, 9B, 15B, 19B, 25B, 29B, 33B, 43B, 47B, 53B, 57B, 61B, 67B, 77B, 81B, 85B, 89B, 93B*
write numbers 100 to 120, 313–316, 317–320